Photographs:
Aisa: 8-9, 10, 11, 12, 14-15, 17, 18, 19, 21, 22-23, 24, 25, 26, 27, 28-29, 30, 31, 32, 33, 35, 36, 36-37, 38-39, 40, 41, 42, 43, 44, 45, 46, 47, 48, 49, 50-51, 53, 54-55, 56, 57, 58, 59, 60-61, 62, 65, 66, 67, 69, 71, 72-73, 77, 78-79, 80-81, 82, 83, 84-85. **Index**: 12, 13, 22-23, 37, 62-63, 87. **Scala**: 74-75, 88-89, 90, 91.

THE BOOK OF
The 15th. Century

Carlos Álvarez Santaló

THE BOOK OF THE 15th. CENTURY
Written by Carlos Álvarez Santaló
Original title: *El libro del siglo XV*
Translated by Dorothy Hill

A co-edition made by
Sociedad Estatal para la Exposición Universal Sevilla 92, S.A.
Editors: Raúl Rispa, César Alonso de los Ríos, María José Aguaza
and
Grupo Anaya, S. A.
Editorial Director: Emilio Pascual
Series Editor: Miriam Rivero Ortiz
Technical Coordinator: Fernando Ramos

1st Edition, April 1992

Text Typeset by Puntographic, S. A. L.
Sol Naciente, 31. 28027 Madrid
Photomechanics: Trescan
Ercilla, 5. 28005 Madrid
Printed in Heraclio Fournier
Apartado 94. Vitoria

© Sociedad Estatal para la Exposición Universal Sevilla 92, S.A., Sevilla, 1992
Recinto de la Cartuja. 41010 Sevilla
© Grupo Anaya, S. A., Madrid, 1992
Telémaco, 43. 28027 Madrid

ISBN: 84-207-4722-X
Depósito legal: VI-286-1992
Impreso en España - Printed in Spain

*T*he Pavilion dedicated to the 15th Century carries a very significant message for visitoris to a Universal Exposition commemorating one year, 1492, and one event, the Discovery of America.

First, we are reminded that there are no magic years and that elements of chance do not simply come together to create a golden year. Secondly, our attention is drawn to the close relationship which exists between a special historical event and all the rest, which to us may seem merely commonplace. In other words, without the sicience, commerce, power struggles, printing, cartography, humanists and craftsmen of the 15th Century, the special voyage which Columbus made would never have been possible. It is a reminder that beneath every surface lie hidden depths, that every apple comes from roots, and that no smile would be possible without a skeleton. The years when marvels happen do not float in time like a miracle. They have to be sown, watered and fertilised during the nine hundred and ninety-nine years which went before. The year 1492 in isolation, without the rest of the 15th Century, would be as absurd as a rose floating in the air without a stem or leaves or roots or soil.

An adventure such as Columbus's seems like a bright idea, a piece of whimsical pigheadedness, which was fortunate enough to appeal to an audacious royal couple and which by chance took place when it did in 1492 and not, for example, in 1392. But the fact is that, although there were adventurous and imaginative sailors, not to mention daring monarchs, in 1392 as well, that particular voyage could not have taken place. On the other hand, it could quite probably have happened in 1470 or 1480. Most people believe that great inventions are often the result of a stroke of luck; that geographical discoveries were made by some wonderful crazy men who took ship one day and set out on the sea to try their luck. This way of looking at great advances in the history of mankind not only does grave injustice to Man, but is also downright stupidity. To see exactly how foolish this point of view is, you only have to think about Man's latest daring adventure, reaching the Moon; then calculate how big a part luck alone played in that success. Surely it is much more reasonable to take into account the centuries of science which were necessary to pave the way for the lunar voyage. Think of the huge investment of political, economic, social and psychological resources which had to be made for the journey to the Moon to be possible. There is no room here for improvisation and no one person has sole responsibility.

In the following pages you will find some open windows which you can look through into that 15th Century and observe some of its exciting new happenings. Hopefully, they will help you to understand how hard it is to be Man. Wealth, culture, fear, suffering, avarice, intelligence, curiosity, ambition and daring — all these are part of Man and each was essential in making possible the year 1492.

HUMANISTS AND PRINTERS

Venice, 1495

People were strolling idly down the Marzaria towards St Mark's. Stopping here and there, they went into little shops, leafed through the piles of books they found there and came out again. There were small books that would fit into a man's pocket and huge tomes on law with the beautiful German lettering they called Gothic, pointed like cathedral spires. The letters all looked newly drawn, standing out from the paper like vines in winter, small and black in long rows on the grey earth. However, not a single one of them had come from an expert hand and a well-sharpened quill. All had been printed a thousand times with ink made from a mixture of oil and lamp-black and lead and copper plates. These books came from a printing house. They had been published for almost fifty years and were still considered a minor miracle.

This year in Venice, the most fashionable book seemed to be a Greek grammar of average size and a little less than 200 pages long. The author was of course Greek. People said that he had emigrated from Constantinople and his name was Constantine Lascaris.

A few knew him as the private teacher of the sons of the Duke of Milan, Francesco Sforza; most people had not even heard of him. What had made this grammar the object of both professional gossip and popular curiosity was not the author but the printer. He was called Aldo Manucio; he was a Roman and had spent only five years both living in Venice and working in the printing trade. You could say that this was his first job as editor. That year there could have been thirty printing houses at work in Venice — one more or

In the 15th century Venice was both an independent state governed by rich merchant noblemen and the most prosperous city in Europe.

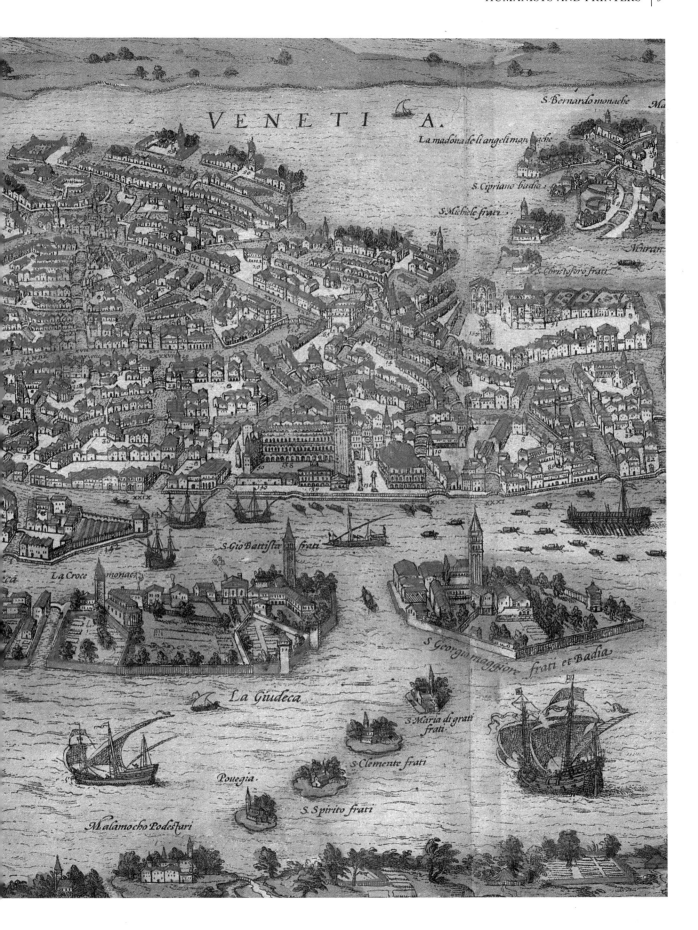

VENETIA.

S. Bernardo monache

La madona de li angeli monache

S. Cipriano badia

S. Michiele frati

S. Christoforo frati

Mura

S. Gio Battista frati

La Croce monace

S. Georgio maggiore frati et Badia

La Giudeca

S. Maria di grati frati

S. Clemente frati

Pouegia

S. Spirito frati

M. alamocho Podestari

less would have passed unnoticed, but not the one belonging to Aldo Manuci. Why? Because it was rumoured that one of his partners was no less a person than the actual son of the Doge.

And old bookseller in the middle of the road raised his arms and shouted to no-one in particular, 'Well, what's so special about this Roman Manuci and what's so special about this grammar? We've been printing books in Venice for 25 years and we've never needed a Roman to come and show us what to do!' 'Not Romans, friend Rufus, but Germans certainly', replied one of his listeners laughing. 'And if Johann de Spira hadn't started printing in Venice in 1469 and after him his brother Vindelino and after him again Nicolas Jenson and John of Cologne, you wouldn't have been able to raise your sons nor buy a piece of silk for your wife like the one she was wearing this morning.'

A few people who had stopped to listen laughed and thumped the old bookseller affectionately on the back. A couple of men then moved away from the group, which was forming a circle, and went on towards the cathedral, very amused. One of them was the man who had spoken to the bookseller. Both were over fifty years old and they walked unhurriedly. From the way they were dressed it was easy to see that they were neither noblemen nor craftsmen. Perhaps they were men who devoted themselves to study or perhaps to business (but they were not rich merchants); or maybe they earned their living with the pen and with words — teachers of children and bookkeepers.

'Master Gasparo,' said the one who had answered the bookseller, 'do you also believe that this grammar is nothing out of the ordinary?'

'You know very well that I don't, Master Antonello,' replied the other, smiling. 'Even if it were not so beautifully printed in Greek and in Latin and even if it were not the first Greek grammar to be publish-

Publishing a manuscript book was a long process as it had to be copied and illustrated as many times as the number of copies. Although those who copied manuscripts were highly-paid specialists, it was easy to make mistakes.

ed in Venice, it would still seem like a gift of wisdom to me. Any book at all is a greater treasure than a galley filled with gold and pepper; but a grammar opens up for us the secrets of languages and so leads us to new treasures of ancient wisdom. Really I...'

'I know, Master Gasparo Egnacio, my friend,' interrupted Antonelli, 'I know that for a teacher of Latin like yourself, who has taught both Latin and Greek in the greatest Courts in Italy, grammar and the ancient poets, their stories and discourses, are more precious than life itself.'

'That's true, very true, and I'm proud of it. There won't be many in Venice who can say that they learned Latin in the first Academy of Florence with masters like Acciaiouli and Rinuccini, although that was a good forty years ago now. And there must be even fewer who have seen and heard, as I have, the greatest and most famous Guarino de Verona, best of all tea-

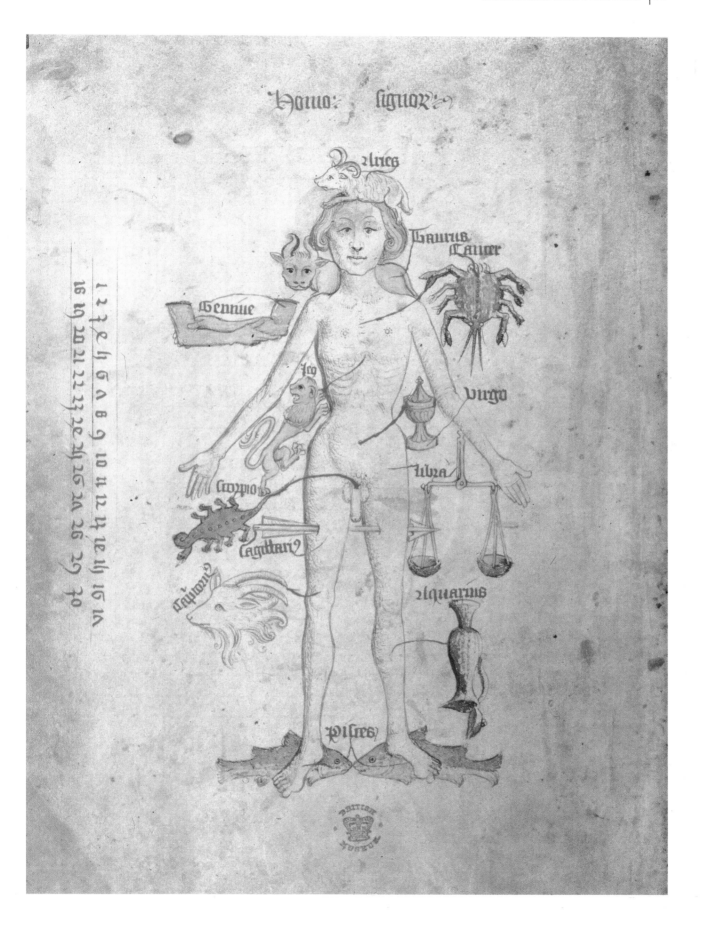

chers. It was only the once, in 1460. I'd have given my whole fortune for the chance to attend his classes, but in those days I had no fortune to give and it was just a lucky chance that I met him on a journey. In spite of that, just to have heard his Latin for one day is worth more to me than a Doctorate from Bologna.'

'Everything is possible, Master Gasparo, since in the Universities, like in the Courts, everything takes time,' sighed Antonello, 'and things don't go any faster in the printing houses, as I well know.'

'You know the printing houses well, Master Antonello, and I the different grammars, something I have always had time and liking for. All my life I have done nothing but learn, teach and read the Ancient Greeks and Romans. But just for the pleasure of knowing the learned men I have dealt with, I wouldn't change my life for a prince's.'

'That depends,' replied Antonello, laugh-

The first company to print books with the new techniques was formed in 1455. The owners were Gutenberg, Fust and Schöffer. The result was the famous 42-line Bible and the no less famous lawsuit between Fust and Gutenberg.

ing. 'There are princes and princes. Some of them have not only got to know the learned men and poets as you say, but can also buy them, their books and you too.'

'That's very true, my friend.'

'That it is, by St Mark! Didn't you have dealings with Prince Lorenzo de Medici in Florence, Master Gasparo? And wasn't it his grandfather, old Cosimo, who gave your colleague Marsilio Ficino a palace in the country so that he could study and translate Plato at his expense? And didn't Prince Lorenzo foot the bill afterwards for the Academy of Marsilio and his friends?'

'That's all true,' replied Gasparo, 'I knew Prince Lorenzo, whom we called the Magnificent, and he was a fair poet and

Although Cosimo de Medici the Elder, was not the first of his line, he was the first Medici to centre all political power around himself in Florence. Until his death he made every effort to turn ''his'' city (an independent state) into the New Athens which the Florentine intellectuals had proclaimed. Banker of popes and head of a vast commercial network covering half of Europe, his role as patron of the arts was both sincere and effective. Though his grandson, Lorenzo the Magnificent, was later to surpass him in fame, Cosim's great virtue was that he was able to reconcile patronage of the arts with big business — which his grandson proved incapable of doing.

almost a philosopher. At that time I was working as secretary to Master Bernardo Ruccellai and I was present at those academic gatherings with Marsilio, Cristoforo Landino and Piero Guicciardini. When the great Pico, Prince of La Mirandola, arrived in 1484, I was already in Naples in the Academy run by Giovanni Pontano and sponsored by King Ferrante. But even though I have dealt with such great men of learning, you shouldn't call me their colleague since I'm only a humble grammarian.'

So saying, Gasparo Egnacio bowed his head and lowered his eyes modestly, though the light in his eyes and the tone of his voice showed clearly that his own opinion of himself was very different from what he had just said. But he had told the truth about everything else. Like many other specialists in what in those days was called *Human Studies*, he had travelled round the Italian Courts, earning his living as a teacher or as a secretary to other more famous intellectuals who could afford to pay him. These experts in classical languages and literature went from Prince to Prince or from City to City, with or without contracts, living off the generosity of rich men of culture and merchants who wanted to educate their sons in the best way possible.

As far as Master Gasparo Egnacio, teacher of Latin, was concerned, after his years in Florence the fame of Pomponio Leto attracted him to Rome in 1475. Thanks to references and a bit of luck, he was able to get into the Vatican Library under the famous Platina. Popes and princes, cardinals and dukes bought the rarest and most beautiful manuscripts wherever they could find them and at prices only they could afford. Someone had to look after them, translate them, study them and publish them. Men like the librarian Platina and his assistant, Master Gasparo, lived off that and from some classes in private houses. Master Gasparo was

not a great specialist, but he was a respectable translator of Greek and Latin and he had important friends. He liked to boast about both facts, especially when, as now, he was looking for work. Using his friendliest tone of voice and taking his new friend Antonello by the arm, he said, 'Master Antonello Rauchfass, let's stop talking about my humble self and tell me about your printing houses and the book business. I buy them and read them, but I don't really know where they come from. To some people this invention, the printing press, seems like a gift from Heaven as they say; but to others it seems like a trick of the Devil to spoil good texts and take the bread out of the mouths of honest copyists who write them with patience.'

'Some do, some don't,' replied Antonello as if he had been stung by a wasp, 'and there isn't much to tell about my life. I was born in Frankfurt and my real name is Gottfried. My family are merchants and businessmen and have always lived between Strasbourg, Nuremberg and Cologne. An uncle of mine known as John Rauchfass the Great went into business with the first printing presses. He provided the capital for his partner, one Nicolas Jenson you've already heard me talk about, who back in those days along with other Germans had the most important publishing house in Venice between 1470 and 1485. Even today it's still called simply 'The Company'. There was another partner in the Company too: Mistress Paola, widow of the painter Antonello de Messina, who later married the printer Rinaldo de Nimega. But that's all water under the bridge and I'm sure I'm boring you.'

'Not at all', replied Gasparo, 'but I can't imagine how a converted wine press and some lead plates could so quickly beco-

Though Lorenzo de Medici largely neglected the family business and brought it to the brink of bankruptcy, he proudly cultivated his image as a poet.

The families which governed Florence were not aristocrats but financiers. In the pictures, details from the Cortège of the Medicis *by Benozzo Gozzoli.*

me such a big business that it could be called a Company.'

'From what I've always heard, when the printing press invented by the master silversmith Johannes Genfleisch von Gutenberg appeared in Maguncia, it created quite a stir and made a lot of money. This von Gutenberg needed a partner with capital so that he could print his great Bible in 1455. This partner was called Johannes Fust but he ended up seizing the inventor's business and his merchandise.'

'Friend Antonello, I'm confused hearing you talk about capital, partners, companies, seizure of property and lawsuits as if we were among merchants from Bruges. What is this printing? Is it work for cultured, studious men or a market for traders who treat the works of Cicero as if they were yards of cloth and the wisdom of Aristotle as if it were a sack of Portuguese pepper?'

'Calm yourself, Master Gasparo Egnacio, and lower your voice — those soldiers are looking at us. In those days everything was business and without money you wouldn't even get anyone to copy you a manuscript by hand, even if it was as short as the 'Deo Gratias'. You could get nothing without paying, not even a pardon for your sins, as the saying goes. Think of my employer Aldo Manucio who is a learned man as excellent and famous as your Guarino or as the Prince of La Mirandola, his great friend. Ermolao Barbaro, himself, the greatest humanist in Venice respected and loved him when he was alive; he died two years ago and will be in glory with his Virgil and his Cicero. Well, this very year 1495, such a learned man as

Aldo has just formed a Society and Company with the printer Torresani and with Pierfrancesco Barbarigo himself, son of the Most Serene Prince who governs Venice and who is no less than the King of France or even the Emperor, for that matter. And if that wasn't the way things work, where else would Master Aldo get the money from to publish all the works of Aristotle, as he would like; how, when the paper alone for three hundred copies of a single volume costs not less than one thousand ducats?'

'I understand that, Master Antonello or Master Gottfried, and even more so since as you know, I'm trying to get a job with Master Aldo Manucio as proofreader — that is, if he hasn't already got someone more capable.'

'You will get the job, Master Gasparo, because I well know that there is nobody more capable. The task of comparing and correcting texts is for those who know language and grammar and who have read the works of the Ancients. It isn't work for little students or casual workers, but rather for experts like yourself and Master Aldo, who has to do it all by himself now.'

'And you, Antonello, can you not help Master Aldo with this?'

'Not with this, no, because although I can read and write and know quite a lot about arithmetic, I have not studied enough. I grew up amongst ink and printing presses and have only an average understanding of the bad Latin that the monks write. When I came to Italy, I did so with Masters Sweynheim and Pannartz who brought the first press, first to Subiaco and then to Rome. I worked there in Rome with the master printer Ulrich Hahn and the publisher Andrea de Bussi and that was in 1467. When I left the lead plates and the presses, I took up bookselling so as not to move too far from what I knew. I have sold books in Florence with the famous bookseller Vespasiano da Bistici, who was bookseller to the Medicis back in 1480. Five years later I came here to Venice to the bookshop of Madiis. Just see, Master Gasparo, if I am fit to correct a page of Aristotle or a letter of Cicero with a background like that. You take the job, it's just right for you, and Master Aldo will pay you whatever is right; it won't be less than three ducats a month and could even be nearer five or six.'

'Friend Antonello, it may be that I will pay with all my knowledge and more if Master Aldo is nearby to correct me if I make a mistake.'

'You can bet your life that he will be near and even on top of you, because to him to change one letter is a worse crime than stabbing a bishop. I have my own job which is to travel wherever Master Aldo sends me to bring back the manuscripts he needs and to have them copied. The world is wide and I have travelled it well, even more than an agent of the Fuggers.'

While chatting and walking, they had arrived at Aldo's printing house and went inside to look for him as Antonello had promised. He was not there and while they were waiting for him, Gasparo asked quietly:

'Excuse my impertinence, friend Antonello, but tell me: is this business secure and profitable?'

'Well, to tell the truth, Master Gasparo, it could be worse, although everything depends on money and on luck. At first, because it was a novelty, it was easy to make a profit and business was good. Many came thinking it would be all plain sailing. Until 1475 or a little later, many pockets were filled here, in Rome, in Paris and even in Milan. Now times are harder. The paper and the lead are very expensive and the workers are better paid than those who earn well in other jobs. In fifty years they've published more than 30,000

titles, and that's a lot of books. Everyone wants to sell, but not everyone wants to or is able to buy. Fifteen years ago one of the big partners in the Company died — the same Nicolas Jenson that my uncle lent the money to. In his will he left four thousand ducats and that was a lot of money. Now if we look at the will of an average mercant in this city, it won't be much less than one hundred thousand ducats. A spice merchant can earn forty thousand ducats a year with his saffron and his pepper, even though he may not be able to read. So you see, Master Gasparo, printing puts food on your plate but it doesn't make you as rich as some people think.'

'That's right, Master Antonello, and it makes many people poor. But every book printed is a tribute to the great masters of Antiquity and an assurance of knowledge for us modern men.'

The man who had just spoken was Master Aldo Manucio, who had come unnoticed into the workshop. When they saw him Antonello and Gasparo bowed respectfully.

'Come, my dear Antonello, introduce me to your friend, who comes from Naples; and let's find out how my friends there are. Perhaps he can tell us about that young poet I've heard about and who I seem to remember is called Sannazaro.'

While he was talking he had taken them by the arm and was leading them towards the inner rooms.

At the same time a galley was setting out on the open sea. In her were two big boxes of books bearing Master Aldo's trademark, which was a dolphin surrounding an anchor. In Rome Paolo Cortese, leading light of the intellectuals, famous humanist and greatly admired teacher of the Court of Pope Alexander VI Borgia, was waiting for them.

The best customers were the universities, as they required large numbers of specialised books. With the press, prices became more accessible.

NAVIGATORS
AND ASTRONOMERS

Palos, 1492

The sandy path shifted about in the wind. The mule, getting on a bit in years, had bad bones and strange habits. It walked with a list to port because one of its hind legs was giving strong hints of rheumatism or worse. To balance itself the animal stretched out its neck to the right in such a way that seen from the front it presented a rare sight. If you saw it you would not know whether to laugh at it or pity it. It had travelled too many miles and eaten too few oats in its lifetime, but walking on the soft sand of the marshlands was good for it and it had now seen a bit more of the world than when it was sold in Alburquerque in Portugal. The muleteer, its previous owner, said his name was Couto. He said over and over again —at least six times— that he would never let such a noble animal and one for which he felt such affection go to just anybody because there are heartless men who believe that a mule is even lower than an infidel and who beat them with sticks and lashes.

—Then in that case perhaps an animal can be greater than a man — always supposing he is an infidel, of course? asked the buyer, laughing.

—If he is an infidel, then that's true for sure and I have heard it repeated many times by an abbot I often visit. Since there was a mule at the manger in Bethlehem, it follows that all his descendents are as Christian as canons.

At the time and even now the traveller was not sure whether the mule-driver was speaking seriously or making a sly joke against the clergy. He paid well, even though he knew all the time they were robbing him, and the following day he set off

Father Marchena and Columbus often met at the La Rábida Monastery.

Right, a 15th- century Mudejar cloister at La Rábida.

for Sagres on Cape St Vincent, where he had a relative and some business to do. Who that relative was, though, and what the business was about has nothing to do with this story. However, one month later Pero Branco, for that was his name, passed through Lagos on route to Ayamonte where Andalusia begins, depending on who you are and how you look at it.

When they reached a crossroads Pero Branco went straight ahead — which was lucky because, if he had left it to the mule to decide, they would have ended up in Huelva. He passed close to Palos when the sun was setting and stopped beside a cross built of bricks and a well which was solidly-

Spices (pepper, cloves, nutmeg) were indispensable for preserving food and as ingredients in cooking. They were also used in medicine. Imported from the East und much sought after by traders, they were literally worth their weight in gold.

Caravans bringing silk, drugs and spices from China travelled to the coast of the Eastern Mediterranean and the Black Sea. Discovering a sea route to the East was essential for European trade.

Canais

Cafa

Sinope

Trebizonda

Constantinopla

Alepo

Chipre

Bagdad

Bodas

Beirut

Libo

Bere

Damasco

Basora

Jaffa

Alejandria

built of the same material, watching the
estuary turn red and purple. Then he
asked directions and after only two different replies he took the sandy path and
went straight towards the monastery. As
he jogged along he was counting the pines
and calculating how many could be used
to build a smallish boat. He was probably
thinking like this because of the jolting mo-
tion of the mule which put him in mind
of travelling on the open sea. It was Spring
and it smelled of the best things in the
world, which are the sea and pine trees.
And then, because you cannot stop your
thoughts, the Portuguese Pero Branco
started remembering his father and how
his father had once said to him while they
were sitting on the cliffs above Sagres looking at the sea in the distance:

—If you ever need to — and you never
know when that might be — and as long
as you have the desire and the money, take
a boat and go to Palos beside Moguer and
Huelva where two rivers join into one.
There are people who call that river the
Tinto or red river because it still has blood
of the Moors in it. When you are there ask
for the pilot Juan de Mafra and tell him
you are my son. He will help you in any
way he can because it's a kind of rule between sea pilots. Those of us who have sailed on the Ocean have experiences which
bind us together.

This father was Joao Branco and his
father in turn was one Fernando Gómez
who had moved from Cáceres to Santarem.

Thinking about this and a few other
things besides brought him to the door of
the monastery which is called La Rábida.
It was neither big nor well-made, at least
not compared with some that Pero Branco had seen.

*Portuguese expansion was
mainly due to Prince
Henry the Navigator, who
promoted journeys of
discovery, and later to
King John II (right).*

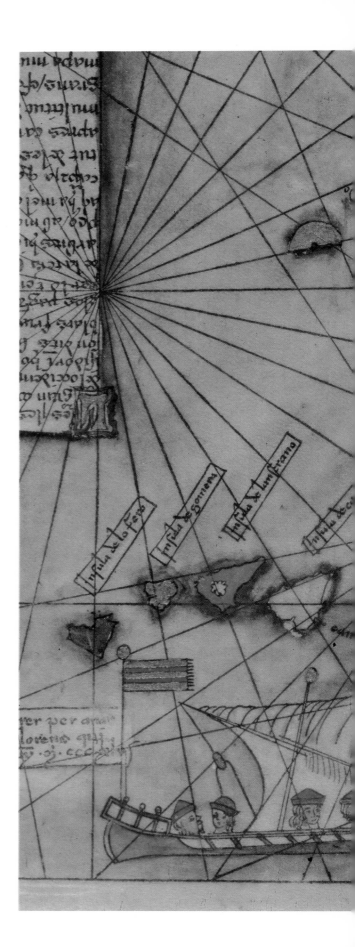

When the friar came out Pero scrambled together all the Latin he knew and taking off his cap murmured:

—*Dominus vobiscum etiamque Sancta Maria, mater nostra.*

—*Gratia plena, laudatque semper. Pax tecum,* —replied the monk.

—I speak Spanish well, your Reverence, because my grandfather, an old Christian, spent time in Extremadura. I am Pero Branco, a pilot and a Portuguese. I am bringing a letter for Father Marchena from a friend of his, a Florentine physician and mathematician who was in Sagres a month ago. His name is Opicino Vesconte and his master was Paolo Toscanelli whom they also call the Cosmographer.

—You are very welcome, brother Pero Branco, for I am that Father Marchena and even if you only arrived hungry and sleepy I would offer you hospitality, as is required by Our Lord. Since you are also carrying Master Vesconte's letter I will give you this hospitality as if you were a close friend, just as if Master Toscanelli himself were standing here this very night.

While they were talking they went in through a patio and a low, narrow cloister. By the time the foreigner had heartily eaten the cheese and the olives and drained a litre of young wine, Father Marchena had already read the letter and pulled his bench close the table.

—Master Vesconte says that you are a first-rate pilot, a great expert on Guinea and a very good subject of King John II.

—He is called the Perfect and he is as good a gentleman as his talents proclaim him to be. I am a pilot of the sea and of the ocean and I believe I come from Santarem. Moreover, I am as good a Christian as any man or even better. For when your foremast has been brought down and the sea is buffeting you along by the nape of the neck you have no more protection than Saint Mary and her Blessed Son, Our Lord. The ocean submits to no lesser authority than theirs.

The Portolanos were the first sea charts of navigation used in the Mediterranean. Those drawn in Genoa and Barcelona in the 14th century were the most famous. Right, a copy of a Catalonian Atlas drawn in 1375.

—We are all in the hands of God, brother Pero, whether our nape is wet or dry. Tell me, how is Master Vesconte?

—He is old and ailing but always buried in his celestial maps and his books. He knows so much about the heavens that he seems to be a pilot rather than a physician, but that is not to be wondered at since these physicians use the heavens so much to chart the insides of men and to know about their humours and their fortunes. So it is not surprising that they know the stars better than Your Reverence knows his monks.

—That is quite right, Señor Pero, but there is no great merit in that because it is easier to know about the twelve constellations than it is to know a single friar — said the Franciscan friar, laughing — And tell me, who is this friend that Vesconte writes you are going to visit in Palos?

The discovery first of the coast of Africa then of America led to the new idea of a familiar world centred around the *Mediterranean and the Red and Black Seas.*

—He is an old pilot who was a friend of my father's. He is called Juan Rodríguez de Mafra and I think he will offer me hospitality because of that friendship, or if not for that because of the little six-litre cask which I am bringing him from the Crown vineyards beside the Guadiana. And should the occasion arise, I will talk to him about some business which should be worth a few ducats to him.

—Yes, that he will do, Señor Branco, because he's a good man and an even better Christian, and he was a first-rate pilot round about Guinea and the Canaries. I shall be pleased to see him if you both come here one day to talk about maps and the stars, but not about business which I cannot grasp. Although I am not as good as Master Vesconte, I know a fair amount about astrology and about Ptolemy. Another pilot would bear me out on this — he is a countryman of Paolo Toscanelli and perhaps you know him since he lived a long time in Portugal. He is called Colón or Columbus; as good a sailor as he is a Christian, if you do not pay attention to the gossip of jealous people. He has sailed the Mediterranean as far as Chios, the Ocean as far as Thule and the African Sea as far as La Mina.

—Actually I do know something about Columbus and about his brother Bartholomew as well, though not because of the treaty. When we came back to Lisbon with Diaz a couple of years ago in 1488 I saw him in the port, although I was not able to speak to him because I had rather a bad fever. Batholomew is the younger brother and I haven't heard anything about him for a few years. Although he isn't a pilot, he is certainly a good cartographer and makes a living from the *mappa mundi* which he draws and from the portolan charts too, with their wind roses and courses, all decorated with fabulous fish. Christopher or Cristóbal made quite a stir there a few

Astronomy was used in navigation for correcting courses at sea and for calculating the *apparent height of the stars on the horizon.*

years ago — but not when he first arrived. Then he was rowed ashore in the wreck of a ship, although he himself was not actually doing the rowing. After that he lived in Madeira and he was certainly married well — to one of the Perestrellos. Then we heard that he wanted to sail westwards from the Canaries and go straight on to find Cipangu and Cathay. He offered my lord, King John, this new journey but the wise men that the king consulted — I think it was in 1484 — said that such a journey would be impossible because they would have to spend more than a hundred days at sea out of sight of land, which had never been done and which was impossible to do.

— I well know where Señor Cristóbal Colón wants to sail, brother Pero Branco, because he must have explained it to me a hundred times sitting right there where you are now. And their Highnesses, Don Fernando and Doña Isabel, the Catholic Monarchs of Castile and Aragon, also know very well; although they have had it explained to them no more than three times — but at great length! And besides them other important gentlemen like the Lords of Medinasidonia and Medinaceli and many wise men of Salamanca also know. Now, in short, the whole of Palos and Moguer will soon know because I've received letters which say that ten days ago their Majesties signed an agreement with Don Cristóbal Colón to maintain him in their service and allowing him to undertake the voyage of discovery he was contemplating. And that will be with God's help and any assistance we may be able to give him here on the orders of their Most Serene Highnesses. That help, as far as I know, will take the form of three boats with their arms and men.

Pero Branco did not even raise his eyes during all this because as a pilot he was used to similar agreements between kings and sailors. He drank slowly and then answered the monk:

The astrolabe was first used in astronomy. By the end of the 15th century it served pilots as a means for calculating latitude while at sea. Shipbuilding lay with extremely specialised craftsmen.

— Reverend Father, I am happy for Señor Columbus if that was what he wanted because this thirst for discovery is like a dog which carries us off as its prey and crushes us in its jaws. And as his life is his own and the Ocean to the west belongs only to God and to our kings as was decided eleven or twelve years ago in Alcaçovas and Toledo, he is entitled to end up where he pleases with the grace of God; and of course seeing that he isn't going to travel from the Canaries downwards and towards Guinea, as they say, because that is Portuguese sea, but from the Canaries outwards which belongs to Spain. But even going where you have a right to, sailing westwards and beyond is a tremendous journey which does not appear on any navigation charts, at least as far as I know. All of us pilots have heard stories and one of them refers to a certain Alonso Sánchez from Huelva who was carried due west in

nul certain nombre des ans. Des causes o
du deluge. selonc la bible · et · av · av ·

Vant noe ot chiut cens
ans il engendra sem · et
cham et iaphet. Et quãt
li homme commenticient
a montepliei sus terre. et
il orent engendie moult

a storm and when he came back they say that he died on the island of Madeira. And now, Father, if you will give me your blessing, I should like to sleep for a while for my bones are aching more than when I sailed round Cape Verde.

—I bless you with all my heart, my son, and tomorrow I will give you letters of introduction for Juan de Mafra and for the physician of Palos, García Hernández. He will be happy to meet you because he knows a lot about the sea. There are even those who say he was in the Azores, although I myself do not believe it.

After that they retired to sleep and Pero Branco dreamed about the little negro boy whom his father brought back from the voyage with Nuno Tristao; that was in 1443 when they reached Cape Blanco. But it cannot have been that journey because Pero was not even born then, so it must have been later when his father came back from Arguin and brought three nuggets of gold with him. The little black boy died but he kept the gold nuggets in a pigskin box along with the compass, the astrolabe and a small piece of coral. Pero Branco always dreamed because when he was a boy his father kept telling him fantastic stories about his journeys, about the island of Palola and the holy city of Timbuctoo and about the negro chiefs who wore ten gold rings on each arm and another ten round their necks, which all together must have weighed around eleven or twelve pounds.

Pero Branco was received in Juan de Mafra's house with respect and joy and after a good lunch, which he really needed, the two pilots sat down on a little terrace with a view of the Punta del Sebo and the mouth of the Tinto — 'tinto' in Spanish meaning 'red' or even 'red wine'.

—I always say, Señor Don Juan, that it is better not to see things that you have heard about in stories because the reality never matches up to your imagination. This river, for example, is not red but the same as all the others.

—I should really have liked to make it run red with wine to please you and because your father also thought the same; but although I have some good vineyards they don't produce that much, Señor Don Pero. And talking of vineyards, there are no better ones round about here than the ones owned by the physician García Hernández who should be here soon.

—Well, while we're waiting for him, Don Juan, tell me more about the pilot Columbus and what he was doing here because we pilots are all obsessed with the same things.

—García Hernández knows more about this because he dealt with Columbus while he was in La Rábida last year with Brother Juan Pérez and Father Marchena; I myself can't walk very well so I seldom go out. I spoke to him once though in the monastery and to me he seemed a man with a lot of knowledge and experience — although, if I may say so, his voice and his manner were a little too abrupt for my liking. He knows Ptolemy and Pliny well and has the writings of Abraham Zacuto and Vizinho almost by heart. He always carries the *Imago Mundi* of Pierre d'Ailly or Alliacus with him and it seems as if he had written the geographies of Marinos of Tyre himself.

—That's rich! — replied the Portuguese jocularly, — since Vizinho was one of those who told King John that the voyage which Columbus proposed could not be made. To tell the truth, what I don't understand is why such a well-travelled man with all his knowledge and his plans came to this spot. I mean, apart from Sagres, this part of Huelva is the furthest place I know from the Court and from where things are happening. I mean no insult to your house because this is one of the best places to live in retirement, but if you are looking for patrons and money it doesn't seem to be so good.

—You're absolutely right, Pero my friend; although some of the Franciscans

you have seen and others too go to the Court in Córdoba, or wherever it might be, just as casually as if they were going to Matins in their own church; and they speak with Queen Isabel as intimately as her confessor, — replied Juan de Mafra, laughing. — But obviously the pilot Columbus didn't know this when he arrived here from Portugal. It's seven years now more or less since he went to the monastery to ask for asylum. He was with his little boy, who now lives with his aunt and uncle in Huelva, or so I have heard García Hernández say. This Columbus must have something special about him which I don't see. For someone who arrived barefoot — as the saying goes — he has been given a lot of protection and support in Court. Even now there are people protecting him who would not give you or me the time of day unless it was at the ship's wheel and even then only if the main mast was broken. For example, Cardinal Mendoza himself who is the Primate of all Spain and whom they call the third king, for one; then there is the Chief Treasurer of the Court, Don Alonso de Quintanilla; and also Prince Don Juan's teacher, Father Diego de Deza, Professor at Salamanca University.

— With these patrons, Don Juan, he could easily go to Cipangu if the Ocean lets him — even to the moon if he could fly! — added Pero Branco.

— Well, even these patrons, not to mention Father Antonio Marchena who is a friend of the queen's confessor, Brother Hernando de Talavera — who is going to be a bishop if he isn't one already — and His Excellency the Duke of Medinaceli, and Father Juan Pérez who also was the queen's confessor, weren't enough. Three months ago Pilot Columbus had no more than fine words and a place at the table of Treasurer Quintanilla in the Court of Santa Fe. He has been trying since the monarchs heard him in Alcalá de Henares six years ago and, as far as I know, a council of learned men has vetoed the journey three times. Along with the veto in Lisbon that makes four rejections and all this because of the maps of Ptolemy.

—But how can that be? I mean, it's enough to say *no* once. If you say it three times you seem to be more doubtful than certain.

—I don't know why, unless it's because the war against the Moors in Málaga, Granada and Almería kept heads and money tied up and the monarchs on horseback. Cathay was a long way away, Granada was just in front of their noses and you load cannons with gunpowder, not pepper. Having new islands and the gold of Marco Polo might give our rulers pleasure, but having Granada is essential. But in the end things worked out; as Father Marchena told you, now Columbus has his contract and his agreement with their Catholic Majesties, Don Fernando and Doña Isabel, whom God protect and prosper. It seems that Columbus will get his boats from here. It's not quite so certain where the men are coming from because there are never as many sailors keen to sign up for voyages to the unknown as there are for journeys to the Canaries.

The physician García Hernández had read Father Marchena's note and arrived just then.

—Pilot Pero Branco, — said the doctor, — it's an honour to know a man as talented as you are and one who has sailed more leagues on the Ocean than I have maxims of Hippocrates in my head. It seems that these days there are nothing but pilots and conquest, so I am honoured to know the one and thank God for the other, especially as they are conquests by our Catholic Majesties. For, as you know, they entered Granada at the beginning of the Year of our Lord 1492.

—It will be fortunate, Señor Physician, — if this is the end of the Crusade; it was high time we kept the infidels on the other side of the Straits. I heard about it in Portugal. It's such a serious business and a just triumph that even your neighbours rejoice in it; they look upon it as their own affair and one that affects the whole of

Using his influence, Father Marchena, Queen Isabel's friend and confessor, ensured that Columbus's plan was swiftly presented at Court. Above, Columbus with his son, Diego, arriving at La Rábida. Right, Father Marchena's room.

Christendom. As far as my leagues travelled on the Ocean are concerned I am willing to believe that you have far more than five thousand maxims in your head, just as I have sailed many more leagues than that from Lisbon to the Cape of Good Hope.

—I am not sure if I know as many maxims as that, Señor Pilot, — replied García Hernández, — but at least I hope they are the truest ones. But at the moment that is not important; I only want you to tell me about your journeys along the coast of Africa, if you are willing.

—Well, Señor Physician, just listen to my story. In 1460, the year when my Lord Henry the Navigator died, I was on a boat

with Pero de Sintra and we reached as far as Sierra Leone and I still remember a certain Messire Cadamosto, a Venetian who came along with us, and all the time he was asking about the sugar trade... and while I'm on the subject of business, does anybody know who is going to pay for this voyage of Columbus and how much it will cost?

—I have read in Brother Antonio de Marchena's papers, — replied the physician, — that the monarchs are going to put up half, which will not be less than a million of *maravedis*, and Columbus is going to put up a quarter, which is the same as saying that the Genoese of Seville, Di Nero or Berardi, will put up that amount because they are going to lend it to him. The rest will have to be found by Palos — but that is going to be decided by the judges and has nothing to do with us.

They went on talking well into the night and did not always speak well of people, because men who steer ships have loose tongues and loud voices and have little respect for what is not concerned with the sea or their own profession.

In the street below two young boys ran about shouting. One of them was called Antón de Alaminos and the other Gonzalo Guerrero. Both of them would be famous in history.

SOLDIERS OF FORTUNE
AND PEASANTS

Treviso, 1476

Going into the little inn, Alberico tripped twice over a stool but not even once over the small black and white dog asleep in the corner. He tripped because there was not much light and because he was old. Perhaps he also tripped because he limped badly with his right leg and made not the slightest effort to hide it. How badly he limped depends on how you look at it. The fact is that the sword slash which almost cut his leg right off was deflected in time by some metal on the skirt of his armour. Being a lucky man, he did not die. Nor did he die in that insignificant battle when a German horse kicked him in the head and knocked out his eye, not very cleanly at that. That could have been another reason why he tripped.

About sixty years old (more rather than less), Alberico had brushed with death five times; four of these on the field of battle and the other in a fight during a card game when a couple of good-sized knives suddenly materialized. He could only attribute still being alive at this age to his good luck and, as he always said to anyone who invited him to a few drinks, to a miraculous copper medallion of Our Lady which he had always carried on him. The fact that the medallion had fallen off into the river during his first battle only showed that Alberico had a poor memory and was a good Christian. He had been a professional soldier, always for hire, who — as he said — could tell a good captain by the noise his armour made when he mounted his horse; and better still by the money he paid when the contract was signed. He never said *contract* because to him the word smacked of commerce and haggling; he always said *condota*, which is the Italian word used to describe the contracts signed by the leaders of mercenary soldiers with the Princes, City-States or with the Pope.

Those who signed these contracts were called Condotieros and those who enlisted with them, like Alberico, were soldiers of fortune fighting for money and adventure. The empty eye-socket and the crippled leg were a question of luck. Life was hard in Italy in those days, but it has always been hard whatever the age and a soldier of fortune had a chance of reaching old age if he was clever, was lucky and of course managed not to let his lucky medallion fall into the river at the first opportunity.

The inn was in Treviso, which at that time was a very small village to the north of Venice and very close to it; a little *above* Venice its inhabitants would say, winking because they assumed it was a joke any stranger would understand. Alberico, who had signed his first contract almost fifty years before, was on his way to somewhere and had stopped in Treviso because the mule, like himself, had a leg which was not quite right. When he signed his contracts he would draw a big cross, which was all

For some war was a profession in 15th-century Italy. Some foreign mercenaries, such as the Englishman Hawkwood, created veritable shools of military tractics and techniques. Despite the use of gunpowder, the cavarly continued to be fundamental in warfare.

he knew how to do, and the captain signed underneath because the captain knew how to write — he knew a lot of other things as well, too many in fact. And so fast did he sign contracts that in the same month they could be hired to fight first for,

then against, the same faction, Prince or City.

Like all the rest, the village had little food, a little money, a good church and some bad houses. There were very few young people because most of them went to Venice to learn about the world, which for the majority meant knowing Venice and no more. Alberico had learned only a little about the world, or a lot depending on how you looked at it. Although he had never left Italy, he had trudged all over it from north to south and from east to west. He had once thought of signing on the Genoese galleys at a time when he was still neither one-eyed nor lame, but the fact is he got drunk the night before and the galley left without him. So the world Alberico had travelled included neither Turks nor Moors, no fair and white-skinned Swedes like the statues in some cathedrals. But in his opinion there were enough odd types around without needing others, especially pagans.

City walls and fortresses offered the greatest degree of safety. Though artillery was used, its high cost and primitive technology left it at a disadvantage when faced with fortifications which needed to be breached or besieged. Right, an Italian miniature of the construction of a fortress.

So it was a fact, and nothing to be ashamed of either, that all his travelling had been done with one foot in front of the other, except one time when he had taken the horse from a Frenchman killed on the battlefield near Naples. The dead man still held the reins in his hands and perhaps that is why the horse had not gone off with the others amid the smoke and the shouting. What a pity it was that the horse had been killed ten days later by a spear-thrust from below.

That is how things stood when the innkeeper came forward to serve him and to bring candles because it was getting dark early as is always the case in winter.

'What can I do for you, sir,' he asked

out of sheer habit and without much interest.

'Not "sir" — I am neither your master nor anybody's — but you can bring a traveller some wine,' replied Alberico. 'I'm cold, like everyone else, and this damned leg is killing me. Anyway, the wound was worth a lot of money to me and I've no cause to complain about it; there are others with better legs who have travelled less.'

'So, sir, you are a soldier?' The innkeeper now looked at him more closely for it was not common in those days for a soldier to reach old age, even if he was lame and minus one eye. Besides, he was beginning to suspect that it was not going to be easy to get his money from someone whose boots were in such a bad state.

'I am hardly anyone at all, far less a soldier; unless horses can now put on their saddles and swords cut by themselves. In the past, yes, I used to be a soldier and no mistake — a famous Condotiero. And after the battles I rewarded my men, filling their helmets with gold coins while they cheered me.'

Alberico, as was his habit (although he certainly was not alone in this), has just told three lies one after the other and pretty big ones at that. He had never risen as high as Condotiero and, although he once carried a very beautiful flag, that did not give him the right to climb so high and so quickly. He had never given a gold coin to anyone, although he had seen some; and for that matter he had never received one either before or after a battle. As for the cheering, he had heard that once in Milan and had found it really exciting. Truth to tell, after the battle he was so beaten up,

The mercenary was as common a figure in the 15th century as a man of any other trade. He signed a contract with his captain and lived off his salary and the proceeds of plunder. Certain noblemen also chose this precarious profession as a way of making their fortune.

dirty and bloody, that if it had not been to curse or spit out a broken tooth, he would never have opened his mouth even if he had seen the devil, far less to cheer.

As they were alone and there was no sign that business was going to improve since it had started to rain, the innkeeper sat down with his customer (seeing he was not a gentleman it was all right to do so), ready to kill time.

'Then you'll have seen a lot, Mister Soldier, and known Lords and Cities. Have you seen the Pope?'

'I've certainly never seen the Pope. I wouldn't lie to such a good man as you seem to be just to make myself seem important. But as for the rest, I've seen all there is to be seen in a Christian country and I've known who I should know; and may God punish me if that is not the whole truth. Innkeeper, I am called Alberico Lando and I'm a Florentine. My father was a soldier with the famous Condotiero Carmagnola, whom you may well know as he was executed in Venice after serving as a victorious general; that happened in 1432.

Though he belonged to the lowest ranks of the nobility, the Knight was considered a symbol of high social standing. Following no leader, he obeyed a special code of honour which bound him to defend just causes. In theory promotion to a higher level of the nobility was won through valour and virtue. In 15th-century Italy the knight was often confused with the soldier of fame and fortune. Firearms, the practicality of capitalism in life and the submission of the nobles to the power of the state brought an end to such a way of life, although the ideals of adventure, justice, valour and honour inherent in the life of the Knight remained alive.

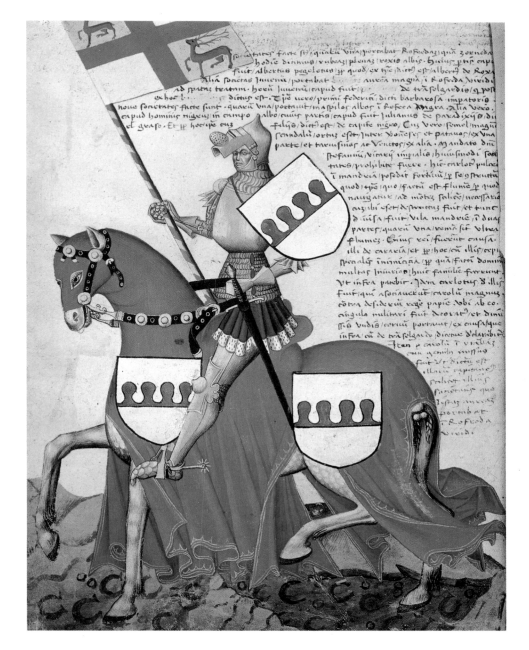

'Yes, I remember,' replied the innkeeper. 'And I also remember that it was publicly announced that he died as a traitor. I was just a child but I remember a blind man coming with a ballad about his famous battles and his death. He sang it in the public squares for money and I heard him.'

'I don't believe he died because he was a traitor,' broke in Alberico raising his voice, 'but because of his victories. Many years later I heard old Colleoni singing about it in camp while he was rubbing down his horse. He said that a Condotiero who is too successful frightens whoever hires him because he thinks that no salary or palace or statue (all of which the Cities and the Princes give to their Condotieros) will seem enough, seeing as how he could have the whole city for himself. I believe that too because this war business is more dangerous than the one with the ships which sail to Alexandria. If you don't win or are beaten, you lose the contract and you're lucky to get out of it with your head on your shoulders. If you win too often or too quickly, they get suspicious that you want to be lord and master of everybody and everything. If they can, they'll sack you and you can kiss your gold and your palace goodbye. If they don't dare to sack you, they'll try to charge you, execute you or have you murdered. In the case of that City which didn't know how to repay the repeated victories of its Condotiero because nothing seemd good enough for him, they decided to kill him, give him a princely funeral, monument included, and name him patron of the City. I was serving with Jacopo Piccinino in Naples when they threw him from the tower where he was held prisoner, on the orders of King Alfonso who had hired him; and that was no more than eleven years ago.'

'And they all end up that badly?' asked the innkeeper, beginning to look at the old soldier with more respect.

'Far from it, far from it. I've known ones with better luck and more skill who have been Princes and Dukes. Well, I know them because I've served in their companies and taken their pay. I, Alberico Lando, fought under the banner of the great Bartolomeo Colleoni until Venice banished him and broke his contract in 1452. I was thirty-six years old then and could have brought down a horse by bending its neck. By the way, this Bartolomeo died only last year, 1475, and I heard tell that in hard cash alone he left more than two hundred thousand ducats.'

'That's a lot of money.'

'It certainly is. With that much you could buy all the land from here to Venice. My first chief, Francesco Sforza, who married the daughter of the Duke of Milan, Lord Filippo Maria Visconti, and who later became Duke and Lord of Milan, left even more. That was in 1450. It's not surprising that he rose so high being the son of my Lord Mussio Attendolo.'

'Who was this Mussio, then?' asked the innkeeper. 'Some very high nobleman?'

'He wasn't born noble, though after-

Socially, men such as Colleoni or the Duke of Urbino were the ultimate ''warlords''. Although the latter, who married into the Sforza family, was a condotiero *and owned only* a small amount of land, his ''court'' was one of the most cultivated in Italy (1450-1508).

wards he became so; but the Condotiero Mussio Attendolo Sforza, according to many, was the hardest, shrewdest, bravest man and most expert in the business of war. I should know because I became a soldier with him in Florence in 1431, cleaning the sweat off the horses and sharpening swords — I was no more than a slip of a lad in those days. And although maybe it's bad to say so, it's almost certain that Mussio wouldn't have liked to see his son Francesco going into Milan Cathedral on horseback, even though it was the enthusiastic crowd who forced him to. Others say that the grand master of the profession was Braccio Montone, but I didn't know him because he went to Rome. And my Lord

the Duke Malatesta de Rimini, whatever else he was, was certainly no coward either. I joined up with him and was sorry that he had to have a row with his neighbour Montefeltro who was a perfect gentleman and I'm not the only one to say so. I've always looked for leaders who would knock a soldier to the ground with one punch and just as easily read Roman history in Latin. Perhaps that's because I've never had the time nor the desire to learn more than the names of the twenty parts of a good Milanese suit of armour. My Lord Malatesta was very learned and perhaps knew too much; they say he had killed two wives in succession. That could be true and as far as I remember there was also some business to do with heresy and Church matters when the Pope excommunicated him. Actually, I've seen a little book written in Latin verse by a scholar at his court comparing him with the Greek gods.'

'God help me!' said the innkeeper. 'These gentlemen may be well-read but some have the hearts of wild beasts! Speaking of which, I heard that they cut the

Wars between city-states were waged for a number of reasons. Disputes over territory, resources, strategic points or simply the struggle for the prestige of being "king of the castle" among all the neighbours were only a few of the reasons for such wars.

State romano
rum z c. Les fai
de son maniere
raromptes z
nus la fondation de rome

la varrete de mamt duier
licux ou ils ont este fais et
pex extres. Et aussi il vauo
en lanaen tamps petit no
bre de gens lettrez au des

throat of your Francesco Sforza's son in Milan Cathedral this very year, 1476. That can't have been for reading books in Latin.'

'I heard that too, and also that he was crueller than a Turk, as if he were mad. My Lord Francesco Sforza had twenty sons and they didn't all turn out like him.'

'So it appears, God help us,' murmured the innkeeper.

'Amen,' replied Alberico who was getting sleepy. His head was spinning, trying to recall the real name of another of his idols, Condotiero Gattamelata, whose statue he had seen in Padua years before. He knew that he had died in 1443 and that the best sculptor of his day, Donatello, had taken ten years to finish it. Then he remembered the name which was always uttered respectfully in Venice even though he had also been in the service of the Duke of Milan — Erasmo. He was called Erasmo de Narni and, by God, there was no-one among the famous Condotieros more dangerous or more refined. A bad business and a plague this fighting, he thought drowsily, although it doesn't turn out the same for everyone. The big statue of Gattamelata on horseback showed very clearly that he had his two good eyes and his two good legs, not to mention money nor the silver baton which Venice had given him.

'Well, Mister Soldier,' said the innkeeper, 'I myself have travelled round no more of the world than the Treviso countryside and, believe me, it's bad land. Nor have I met any gentlemen other than a few young Venetians who were going to Udine to cross over to the Emperor. My father was a peasant and I was a peasant too, until I lost the land and came here to offer wine and hospitality. When I was young, I pulled the plough like an ox, and two plagues didn't manage to kill me off although, to tell the truth, it was such a near thing that my mother promised St Mark a kilo of wax candles every year if he saved me. I myself think that if there are already plagues and floods which rot the harvest, and taxes to kill people, who needs soldiers like you and Condotieros to kill us off more quickly?'

'So you are a peasant, are you, even though you keep an inn?' said Alberico, waking up. 'Then you know nothing of the glory of war nor the honour of the fighting profession. But if you are an innkeeper, it seems to me you must know something about business. Being a mercenary is no different from any other business and it isn't what you kill that matters, but what you gain with victory.'

'The gains of victory, as you put it, have to be balanced against the losses of defeat. Not everyone is happy when it rains, and the hail doesn't all fall in the same orchard. Besides, killing Turks is one thing; they are the enemy and no mistake, because they aren't Christians nor do they have a Pope, and they seize our galleys and carry off our sailors as slaves if they catch them. But tell me, Mister Soldier, if today you are fighting for the Venetians who are paying you and next year with the Milanese who hire you, how can you kill enemies

The peasant worked the hardest, endured the worst social conditions and lived in the most extreme poverty. He was the butt of all abuse and easily fell prey to famine and epidemics.

who yesterday were your friends? The Pope is the Pope of the Venetians and of the Milanese, and of every other Christian, and the Emperor is the same Lord of one and all, may God protect him.'

'The Emperor lives very far away and as long as he is paid his dues, he won't come down here. The Lords of Milan and of Venice, and those of Pisa, Ferrara or Florence are here on the spot, and here is where the gold, the power and the trade are. Here are the cities and the lands, the vassals and the peasants too. Therefore the war takes place here and everything else is unimportant. And I know it's the same where the Emperor lives, and that Princes, Bishops, and trading Cities wage war continually for one reason or another, in spite of having the Emperor breathing down their necks, as they say. Here in Italy there isn't one king as in France, or two as in Spain (who are married into the bargain because one is a queen, apparently), because the one in Naples can't compete either with the Pope or with Venice or with Milan and hardly even with Florence. So everyone wants to be more important than the others, although no-one can be greater than all the rest. What there is to be won are towns, money, fealty, trade, fame and glory of course. Look here, innkeeper, you know about sowing and wine, but about the business of war you know nothing. There are some who say that it would be better for each man to fight for his own city and his Prince, but I say that the cobbler should stick to making shoes and the tailor clothes. War is a matter for soldiers who know it and love it. Well, let them get on with their job! This, Master Innkeeper, is the job — who can pay, pays and the man who earns the money is the one who knows his trade and is ready to lose his life honourably.'

'That would be fine if they were content with their pay,' replied the innkeeper, surly. 'But I've seen tens, even hundreds, of soldiers like your good self, going round the countryside robbing what there is and even what there isn't and beating peasants as if they were stubborn asses. They make war because it's their job, but for goodness' sake it looks as if all soldiers have two trades, and the second one is that of thief.'

'That may well be so,' replied Alberico, well into his role of one talking to an ignoramus. 'But of course it's because the pay doesn't always arrive; in fact it hardly ever comes if things go wrong. Hunger is the same feeling for soldiers and peasants, and whoever wields the sword eats first. But it doesn't always happen like that, and I've often taken part in triumphal entries into cities which have been saved. The victorious people made us parade with flags between flowers and wine as if it were the patron saint's procession, treating us like heroes and saviours.'

'I know nothing about heroes and I know no other saviour except Our Lord Jesus Christ and perhaps also St Mark. But I know as much about hunger and poverty as if I'd been to the University of Padua. And I know full well that the money to pay you soldiers comes out of my belly and out of my sons'...'

Alberico had fallen asleep, this time properly, so he didn't hear the innkeeper explaining the best way to go if he wanted to reach the Emperor's lands.

Alberico was dreaming that his Lord Colleoni, who had gone up to heaven to assist the archangel Saint Michael, was presenting him with a very fine suit of armour. It was from the most prestigious Milanese factory, Missaglia, and caused terror just by its appearance. The innkeeper, who was looking at him, could not understand how one so old, half-blind and lame could still smile in his sleep.

Although free in theory, the peasant was bound to the owner of the land he worked — whether the aristocrat, the church or the local municipality — whom he was obliged to pay for virtually everything — for the right to work, for having children, marrying and dying.

MERCHANTS AND MONKS

Nuremberg, 1463

When they emerged from the wood, Nuremberg appeared in the centre of the plain, so full of towers that it reminded you of a company of Swiss mercenaries raising their pikes. Somebody once said that there were more than a hundred of them, all pointed. The tops of some were finished off with four little box-like turrets, and more than half of them had a couple of bells — if you could not find bells in Nuremberg, then where? Only one had a clock; one of those clocks that start to sound the hour from sunset. Just then winter sun was tinting the whole town a golden parchment shade which, although very beautiful, did not fit very well with Nuremberg's reputation as the Silver City.

'And the river? But where is the river? Because I don't suppose it can be *that*!'

That was the shining thread passing through the town walls and which from a distance looked exactly like a thread for embroidering the rich cloth of silver which the bourgeoisie of the imperial city wore on red-letter days.

'Praised be Saint Francis, my brother Filippo! There is no river in Nuremberg; there never has been and I don't think there ever will be unless my Father Saint Francis performs a miracle. There are rivers in Bruges, in Amsterdam, in Basle, in Frankfurt, in Mannheim and in Lübeck. In that city ahead of us there is no more than a stream which they call Pegnitz and which couldn't wet us higher than our boots. However, stream or tiny river, one sure thing is that it's enough to turn the wheels of the forges and the ironworks. And there are certainly plenty of those in

Nuremberg was a key point in European trade, especially for copper, silver, tin and zinc. Situated mid-way on the trade routes between *Antwerp and Budapest, it became prosperous through its bronze and brass industries.*

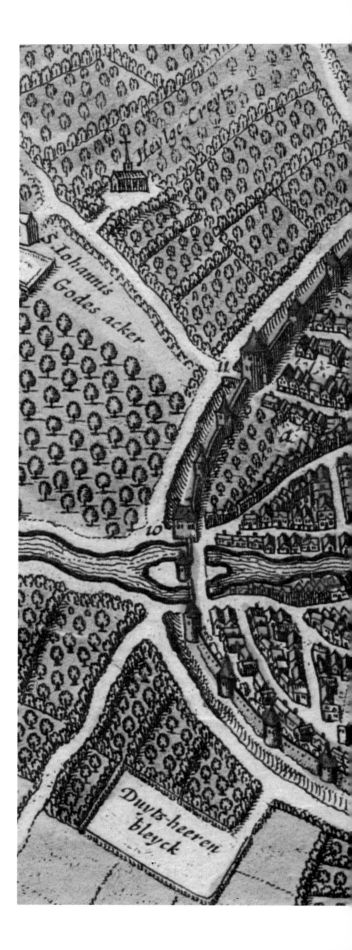

Nuremberg; half the city is a smithy and the other half is a warehouse for silver, tin and copper. There is so much of that here that instead of criticizing their neighbours, the women in the market pull the watchmaker to pieces as he deserves, and feel the bellies of the bronze cannons they cast for the Duke of Milan, as if they were handling a cow in labour. So they say anyway, because the ones I've seen find fault with their neighbours under their breath, and as soon as they see a monk they cluster round him to get some new relic and a couple of prayers and some blessed herbs if he has any. What's more, if they work the bellows in the forge it would be better for a young man like yourself not to get any closer to them than you would get to a horse that had smelt gunpowder.'

The two travellers stood watching the city from afar and the little figures making their way towards its four great gates. Filippo Matteo Strozzi, as his companion had observed, was a young man in his twenties. All the important cities he knew, starting with his own, Florence, had not just any river but a majestic river, and at least half a dozen bridges. Not all the bridges would be as long as in Lucerne, nor as crammed with houses as the one in London, or as full as legends as the one on the Rialto in Venice or with as many boats as in Seville; but they would all have at the very least a chapel in the centre and two

Through the use of machinery, mining techniques improved during the 15th century. Machines were used for pumping water, for working bellows in forges and for smelting and hammering metal. Below, a detail from Mining *(15th century).*

good lanterns on the pillars at either end. In cities, a good river and a good bridge help to order things. Some things are on this side of the river and some things on the other side and everybody knows where to find what he wants. Besides, the importance of things like boat trips and flour mills should not be overlooked.

The companion who had just been explaining things to Filippo Strozzi seemed to be a monk — he was a friar and a Franciscan to boot. He had fifty long years under his habit and wore a beard (which seemed to him to smack of humility), which now had more white than black in it.

The young Florentine was leading a none too good horse, though each of its legs could have supported a church roof and you could have painted a fair-sized

The common people's favourite form of entertainment was the Carnival, a time when the authorities permitted mockery and criticism which would normally have been severely punished. Above, a detail from Lent and Carnival *by Brueghel.*

map of the heavens on each of its haunches with room to spare. The countryfolk called these enormous draught animals 'percherons' for obvious reasons and also 'frisians', after their place of origin of course. The friar was wearing sandals on his feet and carrying no more than a stick, almost as straight and as tall as himself. Seeing the way he raised and lowered it to point things out and how he passed it from hand to hand behind his back, it was almost certain that in time of need it was less than a lance but rather more than just a stick. There was an insignificant braggart with a head wound in Ratisbon, which they had both left two days before, who could testify to every detail of the friar's use of his staff point by point. His respect for the Church had increased enormously and you could say that his first experience of the Order of Saint Francis had been unforgettable. In short, he had learned two important points, both very useful for his occupation of living off other people. Firstly, a friar is not always what he seems nor like the ones he had seen in pictures — fat, useless and cowardly. Secondly, however heavy a holy brother's bag, it was not worth checking it out if the owner was carrying a stout stick. To have learned all that in one single day was not bad going.

The young Florentine forgot all about the monk and, tugging the reins of his huge horse, began walking again.

'Come on, Brother Dolcino, or they'll shut the gates on us and this is no night for sleeping in the open and even less in a mule-driver's inn.'

'Let's go then, in the name of God and my Holy Father Saint Francis, young sir, but never fear that they will close the gates against us before the first striking of the clock. It's even less likely seeing that line of carts from Cologne waiting to get in. There must be more than thirty of them and if a single one is left outside, some guard will lose his hands and his ears. In the twenty years I've been coming this way it's always been like that and today will be no different.'

'You've been to Nuremberg before then, Brother Dolcino,' said young Strozzi.

'Yes, I have, and not only once or even ten times. From Lyons in France to Leipzig and from Antwerp to Venice there can't be many cities my sandals haven't trodden nor many chapels where I haven't preached. I only have to hear the bells to know which city I'm in and from the smell of the market alone I'd be able to go round

Religiour orders, particularly the mendicant preachers (Franciscans), acted as a bridge between the church hierarchy and the common people. Other orders, such as the Dominicans, founded by St. Dominic of Guzmán in 1206, *specialised in university teaching. For their part, the cathedrals represented the faith of the people and the financial power of the Church.*

all of them without tripping over a single corner even if I were blind.'

It is true that Brother Dolcino Casale was no mean preacher and being a pilgrim was only half his task; the other half, of course, was to save the souls of good people. Years before during Lent, he had arrived to preach before the Prince Elector of Maguncia (one of the seven who elected the Emperor). When the sermon was finished, in spite of being such a great bishop as well as prince, he kissed the cord of Brother Dolcino's habit. He also sent a servant to the monastery taking him a goose which weighed a good twenty pounds and a little bag with three gold florins. Nothing

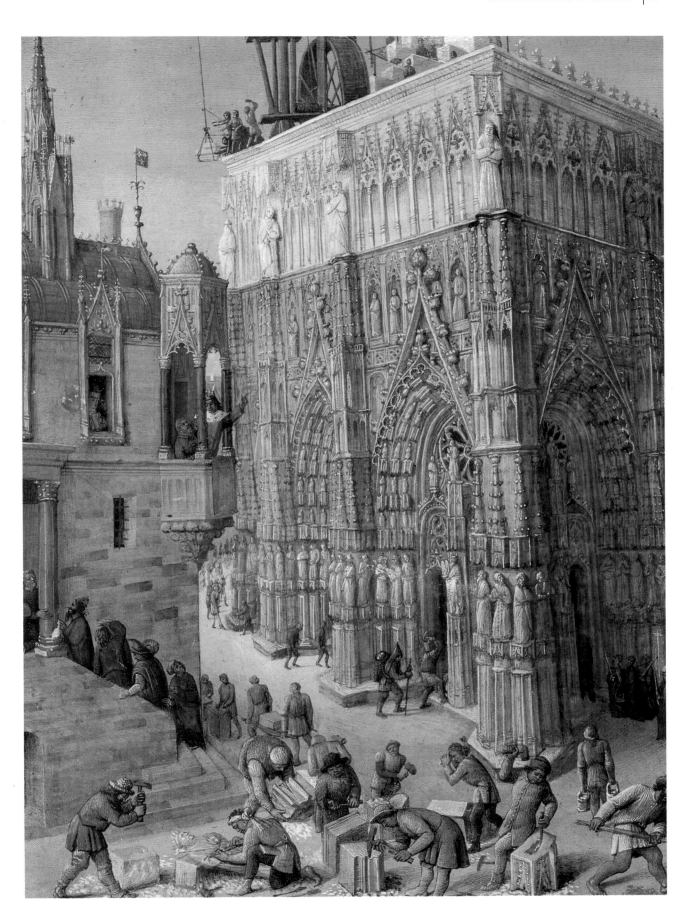

The extremely strong influence of the Popes in the politics of the Middle Ages began to decline during the 14th and 15th centuries. Their spiritual prestige was also affected by what was known as the "Great Schism of the West", when there were three different Popes, each with his own court and administration. This war between Popes was put to an end in 1414 by the authority of the Emperor and the Council. Fifty years later, the Popes had made Rome (the capital of both their kingdom and of Chistianity) into the capital of Renaissance culture. As feudal heads of state, they intervened in both Italian and international politics and, like their neighbours in Florence, Venice, Naples and Milan, held their own courts and patronised intellectual and artistic activities. Their religious life was not always exemplary and their religious interests were all too often overshadowed by their political and financial interests.

Linked to the interests of the great merchants, the first private banks appeared in the 14th century. These facilitated trade by means of documents of credit such as bills of exchange and cheques. Above, Portrait of Cristof Fugger; *right,* The Money Changer and His Wife.

like that had happened since because of certain problems which Brother Dolcino had with his Superior and a few other matters too; but that is another story. He had met the young Italian just outside Ratisbon. Since they were both heading the same way and as Filippo Strozzi was a fellow countryman from a good family and with a fair-sized purse to judge by the size of his horse, he decided to join him on the journey. It certainly must have occurred to him that in such good company he was more likely to dine that night and, who knows, even to have breakfast the following day. He thought, and rightly, that such a polite young man, leading a horse as big as a hermitage and with leather saddlebags the size of chasubles, would not begrudge an old friar a plateful of fish. If

he was right, it would be his first dinner in three days, discounting the crust of stale bread and cabbage soup he had got at the monastery. Fasting is conducive to holiness, but it doesn't do to tempt God, not even if you are a friar, and especially if you are a Franciscan.

Filippo, who was walking beside the bulk of his beast which reminded him of the statue of Gattamelata in Padua, was wondering whether the money he had paid for it in Augsburg might not have been better spent. He emerged from his thoughts hearing the friar's voice close to his ear.

'If your host, old Fütterer, is in the city, you'll have a good plump bed tonight and a good goose for dinner, Master Strozzi,' said the holy man, who used terms like *my brother* and *sir* or *master* according to inspiration and the sounds of his belly rumbling with hunger. 'I'm saying that because I know his house and his kitchen which can be no worse than the Doge of Venice's, His Most Serene Prince Pascuale Malipiero. The honourable Jorg Fütterer is one of the ten richest men in Nuremberg, which is to say that our Lord God will have a lot to forgive him for.'

'Yes, he's sure to be there. A month ago he sent a letter to me in his Offices in Augsburg and another to the Great Company's Offices in Ravensburg saying that he was expecting me. I'm bringing him news and, what is more important, money. But you are certainly behind the times, Brother Dolcino. Doge Malipiero died last year and now it is Messire Cristóforo Moro. I am carrying business news from the Offices in Venice; I could even tell you when the galleys arrive from Trebizond and when the Alexandria galleys leave.'

'On the other hand,' replied the friar, laughing, 'if the Pope died today, I wouldn't find out for three months at least and only then if I'm lucky.'

'Well, if you're interested, I can tell you that up to last week at least Pius II Pic-

colomini enjoyed good health according to my letters from Rome.'

'May God keep him in good health, for it's better to have a wise man in Saint Peter's chair than a wolf and may my Father St Francis forgive me for speaking thus of the Princes of the Church.'

'I've known more than one wolf wearing the Cardinal's purple in Florence and in Venice. But tell me, Reverend Father, why you spoke as you did about Messire Fütterer's sins. I've heard that he is never drunk, he has honest habits and fears the Lord, spending money on good works and better convents.'

'I wasn't speaking of sins, far less the ones you mention. Gold and silver are bad bedfellows of virtue. Lending money and getting back more than you lent may be good business, but believe me, it doesn't help much when you die,' replied the monk. He looked out of the corner of his eye at the young Florentine merchant whose surname had been synonymous with money for more than a century in Florence.

'It must help a bit if you leave what is necessary to the Church in your will,' replied the young merchant, very sure of himself. 'And you know very well that in Florence the story goes that the Pope is involved in business deals that would make old Cosimo de Medici blush if he were not his partner and his banker.'

Filippo's smile did not bode well as regards dinner, or at least so Brother Dolcino thought, but the ball was in his court and he could not dodge the issue.

'That may well be, Master Strozzi, although you must admit that your family and the the Medicis have longstanding lawsuits. And even though I'm a friar, I'm

There was no such thing as safety on the highways. Bands of thieves, simple vagabonds and even noblemen ambushed and robbed travellers. Right, The Thief Punished, an illustration from a 14th-century manuscript.

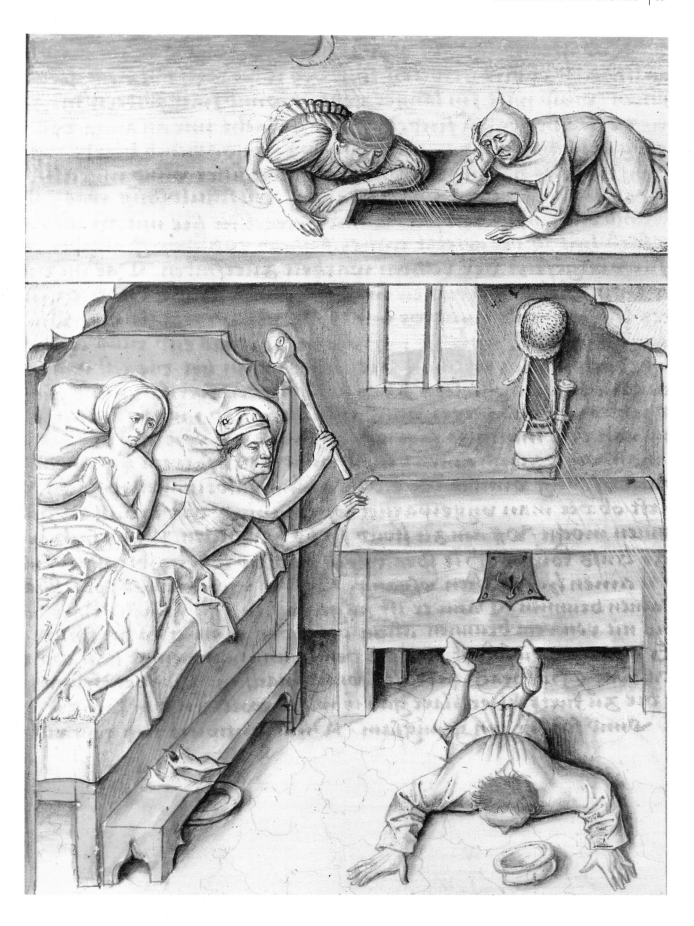

Trade followed established routes, passing through towns along the way. Transportation of goods by sea or river was cheaper but required higher investment. Above, Miniature of the Statutes of the Trades; right, a 15th-century fresco.

not so ignorant that I dont't know the price of a cardinal's hat nor who negotiates the Church tithes in Rome or in Seville. Giving money to the Holy Mother Church is good business since the Lord always repays one hundred-fold, but it's a long road to travel to buy Heaven that way, ducat by ducat. Now, whatever the Pope may do, you must admit that, being metal, money cannnot breed, so whoever lends ten should get back ten afterwards and not twelve or thirteen as if the coins had given birth in the purse during the nine months of the loan.

'Well, I remember reading something else in Antonino of Florence and Bernardino of Siena, and I still seem to remember that two Popes in 1425 and 1455 issued Bulls authorizing loans. And let's not forget that when the Popes were governing the Church from Avignon in France, they devised more ways of lending and collecting money than their neighbours in Cahors who were famous for the marvels they could work shuffling money backwards and forwards. Anything a native of Cahors didn't already know about loans and second loans and fairs, he learned from a Monsignor and even from a Bishop himself.'

'That's very true, young sir, but surely

that must have been to pay for the greatest spiritual needs. Those were bad times for everyone, the Avignon era, and more than a century has passed since then. When all's said and done, I don't want to argue with you for I see that you've read all that's necessary and the Holy Church has better apologists than me. But tell me, didn't you say earlier that you were carrying money to Messire Fütterer? I can't see the bags of coins, and a man like him wouldn't have made you come for the sake of a hundred florins that would fit into your purse.'

'Coins?' Now Philippo Strozzi laughed heartily. 'I never carry coins, only papers. There are 30,000 ducats and more in those saddlebags — all Bills of Exchange and cheques. A good piece of paper with payment dates and signatures is all that's necessary to collect money from Lisbon to Cracow, and from London to Naples. Bags of money are for keeping in iron boxes. A good merchant works more with a pen than with scales, Brother Dolcino.'

'That's right, if you say so, and it will be difficult for the Holy Church to check amongst so many papers where there is usury and where there is only a merchant's honest profits.'

Chatting as they went along, they arrived in front of the two towers of the east gate. There were great comings and goings of mules and their drivers and you could hear curses in three or four different languages, but which everyone understood. Asking the way from time to time and aided by Brother Dolcino's memory, they soon found themselves at Jorg Fütterer's house. They were given dinner and shown into a room with a stone fireplace big enough for a stable for the mighty beast that Filippo Strozzi had bought. A stable only by virtue of its size and not because it was dirty, for that fireplace was as clean as the silver platter that shone in the middle of a black table (which perhaps was not black but dark brown) and seemed like the calm, unwinking eye of some giant fish.

Old Fütterer was in a high-backed armchair with a fur rug over his knees. No-one was quite sure whether he was a Merchant or a Banker because he was both and, according to his enemies, two or three things besides and none of them holy. During that year of 1463 two thousand carts with wool, linen, silver, tin, mercury wood, silk and saffron arrived in Nuremberg, plus some with books and others with armour and spices. A quarter of all this, give or take a little, belonged to old Fütterer, not counting the Bills of Exchange nor the Portuguese sugar, because that came in smaller packets. He brought the silver from Bohemia and the alum from Florence from the Pope's mines, mercury from Castile, cork from Portugal and salt from France. He was an important partner in the Great Company of Ravensburg and of the Popplaus in Breslau. Wicked tongues (and there are many in Nuremberg) murmured that he lent money to the Medicis, which was not true, and that he was a partne of old Cosimo in Bruges, which really was true. But in spite of all that he was an old man and he felt the cold.

Brother Dolcino, who finally had dined properly and as a Fütterer had commanded, was looking rather sleepily at some small scales with triangular pans used for weighing coins which were on the table.

'I don't use them now, Reverend,' said the old merchant.' I keep them as a souvenir of my young days when I sat with them at the Bruges and Frankfurt Fairs and changed all kinds of money at its correct rate — most of the time. Nowadays I could ruin an average city without stir-

Bills of exchange solved the problem of carrying money for trading with. They were importants documents which guaranteed payment at a pre-arranged time and place. Right, Portrait of a Banker by Gossaert.

ring from my armchair and have absolutely no reason to weigh gold and silver if all money now is paper and ink. Sitting here I know almost every day the exchange rates and market prices whether in Siena or Budapest, Hamburg or Barcelona. And if St George's Bank in Genoa alters the cargo of a London-bound ship by as little as one strand of saffron, it won't take me more than three days to find out … perhaps four if the courier is fond of his beer.'

'It seems to me, Messire Jorg,' replied the friar in his most grateful voice, 'that you have more messengers in your service than Saint Michael has.'

'I have as many as I need, Reverend Father, and my partners have as many as they need and we all work together for our mutual benefit, when that is God's will.'

'God's will and when it doesn't endanger profits,' replied the Franciscan, who was beginning to understand something of this labyrinth.

'Every honourable man should get some return for his labour,' intoned the old banker solemnly 'and that is written in the Gospel itself.'

'That is so and it is also written that you should share it with your brothers, as you have just done with this humble servant of the Church.'

'I've done greater things for the Church than give dinner to a friar, Brother Dolcino, greater and far more costly. Three convents in this city and two hermitages, not to mention the Cathedral, will bear me out on that.'

Young Strozzi pulled his chair closer to the fireplace and turned to his host respectfully but smiling. 'Messire Fütterer, Brother Dolcino believes that money should not increase when it is lent and that profits turn men into sinners and hard-hearts.'

'Men are already hard-hearted, with or without profits. As regards being sinners, we all are and it doesn't take money to make us like that. Brother Dolcino has his beliefs and I have mine. It's one thing to preach and another to give bread, but I don't think they have as many scruples in Rome when they sell alum, and Cosimo knows when to put the pressure on prices and credit. Look at this boy, Reverend Father; since he was nine years old when he went to arithmetic school he has been preparing himself to learn about business and be an honest merchant. His family sent him to Genoa, Siena and Venice so that he could learn. He spent three years in Ravensburg as his family's agent in our Great Company and went on learning with old Humpis who was directing it then. He knows the branches we have in Lyons, Antwerp and Geneva and now he's going to spend a year with me here in Nuremberg. Now tell me, Brother Dolcino, if all this time and work don't deserve a good return?'

'May my Father Saint Francis protect us!' exclaimed the good friar, astonished. 'It's beginning to seem to me that it's easier to become a Doctor in Padua and a Master of both branches of Law in Bologna than it is to learn the art of business and the mysteries of the Fairs.'

'That may be', acknowledged Filippo Strozzi, 'but remember what my countryman, Messire Giovanni Ruccellai, and as good a merchant as he was a humanist, wrote: *Squandering his heritage and giving to fools and crazy women makes no man courteous and charming; only Business, well-directed as regards how, how much and where to, makes a man wise and worthy of respect.* He wrote that in his book, *El Zibaldone.*'

'*Regnat avaritia, regnant et avari,*' murmured the friar to himself; then raising his voice said, 'Didn't I hear a little song in the laundry in Frankfurt which went: *However agreeable and lovable your wife and*

Information was essential to merchants; these possessed their own messenger services and were often better and more quickly informed than kings. Right, a 15th-century picture of a messenger.

children may be, profits are much nicer and more lovable? If I may say so, to me that seems like the sin of greed, which is very well explained in the *Summa* of Thomas of Aquinas.'

'He was not a man of your Order, Brother Dolcino, and I suspect he is not the saint you pray to most, but while we're on the subject he also explained very well and in the same book that business profits are lawful, when they are moderate and in proportion to the capital risk and the Merchant's labour', replied old Fütterer the banker, who was not as ignorant as some believed.

'And while you are recalling German ditties, Brother Dolcino,' young Strozzi added, 'see what you think of this one which is sung from Constance to Cologne: *If you want to earn your living, young gentleman, listen to me. Mount your horse and go to the woods. When a traveller comes along, grip him tightly by the throat, be of good cheer and take away all he has. What belongs to one, belongs to two if the second wields the rope and the knife well.* I hope that business doesn't strike you as being preferable to ours, Reverend Father.'

'Don't speak heresy, Messire Filippo, don't offend God and my Father Saint Francis,' replied the friar. 'How could killing and highway robbery seem better to me? But remember, Brothers, that all the money in the world won't help us at all if we can't look up to Heaven joyfully.'

'I cannot look up to Heaven with joy or without,' replied old Fütterer, 'because as this young man's countryman, Messire Alberto Alberti, puts it so well, the businessman must always have his hands stained with ink , and if I spend day and night annotating the accounts in my books, perhaps you can tell me when I'll have time to look up to Heaven. Every time I raise my head from the columns of figures a bundle of fustian disappears, so to speak, and a load of wool passes from *credit* to *debit* as if by magic. The sleeping

The normal market was made up of the shops and workshops of the master craftsmen. Every week, on a particular day, the peasants brought their produce into the city, swelling the size of the market and bringing new life to it. In some towns Fairs were held at certain times of the year and these attracted the richer merchants. The money changer with his delicate scales for weighing coins of gold and silver was a familiar figure at such fairs and markets. Many later became bankers. The market was also the favourite haunt of acrobats, jugglers and story-tellers. Nor was there a lack of scoundrels and petty thieves waiting to take full advantage of the crowds of people amid the hustle and bustle.

trout is carried away by the force of the current and the same will happen to your accounts of souls and in your business of salvation.'

Brother Dolcino realised that it was time to go to bed and soon afterwards took leave of his hosts, received substantial alms and blessed them with all his heart. When he had gone, Filippo Strozzi opened his leather saddlebags and gave old Fütterer the receipts he was carrying along with the

Bills of Exchange, as these signed papers guaranteeing loans and repayments are called. The old man opened the first one on the pile and read aloud: *To Jorg Fütterer, German, residing in Nuremberg. In the name of God; Augsburg, this thirtieth day of March in the year of Our Lord 1462. By authorisation of this first Bill (the second and third not being acted upon), would you kindly pay to Enrico di Baldo of Savoy at the next Nuremberg Fair the sum of thirty-five Venetian ducats at an exchange rate of* *nine pounds to the ducat; this being the amount received here from Giovanni Piccaglio. I remain, sir, Hans Heim of Augsburg.*

'So it will be, with God's help,' murmured Fütterer the banker, 'and Messire Enrico di Baldo will have made his twenty percent from an honest loan; and I in time will make mine, if that is the will of God.'

PATRONS AND ARTISTS

Siena, 1457

His Most Holy Eminence Enea Silvio Piccolomini, standing by the columned window of the Bishop's Palace in Siena let both his eyes and his thoughts wander.

A dozen hand-written books were piled up on a table covered with velvet brocade. Their pages had been transformed by the best miniaturists into small retablos of gold and blue. His Eminence himself had written some of the books: a treatise on educating the young; a manual on rhetoric, an art in which Cardinal Silvio was known to excel as a teacher of consummate skill. This was not surprising as he had been an attentive disciple of Bernardino of Siena, from time to time. He had also penned a History of Bohemia and another about the happily reigning Emperor Friedrich III and *Lives of Distinguished Men*, the last chapter of which had not yet been written — His Eminence felt he should dedicate this final chapter to his own life. Finally there was a slim volume of chivalrous verses, written by the same hand and bound in blue velvet with silver decorations at the corners and on the clasp.

The Cardinal was good-looking (although he remembered having been much more so in his young days) even if his fifty-two years had given him bags under his eyes and added a tinge of sadness to his look.

A very young manservant who had opened the door bowed while he announced, 'Monsignor, Master Massolino da Panicale, whom you summoned, is outside waiting to be received.'

'Show him in and leave us.'

The Cardinal thought, amused, that the

From 1458 to 1464, Enea Silvio was known as Pope Pius II. Although he did all he could to further the cause of the Crusades. As an intellectual, he was a noteworthy humanist. *Right, Enea Silvio receiving the Crown of the Poets from Friedrich III.*

boy still had not got used to using the correct form of address, Eminence, and went on using 'Monsignor', which was correct for a bishop. Actually, Enea Silvio had been a bishop for the past nine years but last year, in 1456, His Holiness Calixtus III had seen fit to raise him to Cardinal of Santa Sabina and converted him into His Very Reverend Eminence. The Cardinal certainly thought that he had advanced very rapidly in his ecclesiastical career but he also believed that he deserved it.

When Master Massolino da Panicale of Florence entered, Cardinal Enea Silvio was just remembering that he had been ordained priest in 1447 at the age of 42. Quite unconsciously he had looked towards a big silver box almost hidden behind the pile of books which held a small crown of gold wire with laurel leaves, now dry. With pride (a sentiment which does not seem appropriate for a Cardinal, but you should never judge a prince of the Church so superficially) he remembered when Emperor Friedrich had placed it on his head, awarding him the prize as Poet.

'Enea Silvio, Poet,' murmured His Eminence to himself, although not so quietly that Master Massolino, bending to kiss his ring, did not raise his head.

'I beg your pardon, Your Eminence, I did not hear your Eminence's words very well since I am a little deaf by God's will, although I am always at the service of Your Very Reverend Eminence.'

'Rise, Master Massolino, and I expect that God's will is less to blame for your deafness than the din of the chisels and hammers in the casting workshops of Messire Lorenzo Ghiberti and Messire Donatello. You were working with them, if I am not misinformed, and believe me, I try to be as well-informed as possible.'

'You are absolutely correct on both counts, Your Eminence. When I was a boy with my father in Florence learning *disegno*, he sent me to Master Ghiberti's workshop. At that time he was starting to cast

the second bronze doors he was making for the Baptistry. That would be, Eminence … that'll be twenty-five years ago and I was in his workshop for nine years. Every day of those nine years I saw and touched a masterpiece. For anyone who has not seen the creation of the world, it's enough to have seen the creation of those doors.'

'Nine years,' thought the Cardinal, 'the same length of time I've been a priest. In those nine years I've become a prince of the Church while Master Massolino has not managed to become another Ghiberti after his nine years.'

He stared at the artist, a sturdy man getting on for fifty years old who was standing with his head slightly bowed.

'Ah yes, Master Massolino, you are referring to the doors which are called *del Paraiso* aren't you? They are certainly a masterpiece, worthy of Master Ghiberti and worthy of Florence. If Paradise needed gates, these would certainly be good enough. Any one of the ancient gods would gladly have agreed to be cast in them in exchange for eternal form and glory. Did you know that the great Lorenzi Bruni gave Master Ghiberti the subjects and the arrangement of the scenes which are depicted in them? In fact, the whole story of the competition and the making of the two doors of the Florentine Baptistry would have been worth an epic poem — another Aeneid, perhaps. It could certainly be done and somebody should do it. Now Masters Ghiberti and Bruni are dead but you and I and many others know very well, Master Massolino, that as long as the bronze doors still stand, the two will be regarded as demigods.'

'Excuse me, Your Eminence, but per-

In 1401 the Florence textile merchants' guild organised a competition to make a pair of bronze doors for the Florence Baptistry. It was won by Ghiberti, who was only twenty years old at the time. In 1425 Ghiberti was commissioned for The Gates of Paradise.

In the 15th century all art forms, from architecture to music, were considered to be halfway between craftsmanship and genius. In practice, this meant that "artists" (who were known as "artificers") could work not on what they wished to work but on tasks for which they were commissioned. Fortunately for them (and also for us) their customers — kings, princes, rich nobles, merchants, bankers, cardinals and Popes — were in most cases men of sufficient good taste, education and wealth to commission masterpieces. On many occasions these customers became the permanent patrons and protectors of artists they considered to be their own; artists whom they not only paid but also allowed to live in luxury in their own palaces and houses.

haps ...' gabbled Messire Massolino surprised and confused, made almost uncomfortable by the Cardinal's last words.

'Demigods, Master Massolino, and you needn't be scandalized. I wasn't born an ecclesiastic and you certainly weren't either. We humanists and artists are brothers in beauty and poetry. I should like you to stop standing there motionless like a country bumpkin in front of Cardinal Piccolomini and recover your dignity as an artist and an expert in front of Enea Silvio, poet.'

'But, Eminence, I cannot ... I shouldn't ... really I ...'

'For goodness sake, Master Massolino, don't talk any more nonsense and stop talking in fits and starts like a startled novice. I've got my Petrarch and my two Lorenzos, Valla and Bruni; you've got yours, Ghiberti and Monaco, your Donatello and for all I know your Piero della Francesca. I would happily exchange my Cardinal's hat for an hour's conversation with Petrarch; obviously I shall have to wait until the resurrection of the dead to fulfil that desire. You, on the other hand, haven't had to wait so long; you have enjoyed the privilege of having been able to see and learn from the artists you admire, complete masters of their trade and their art. This Cardinal envies you that privilege and perhaps also your knowledge of their secrets.'

'For Heaven's sake, Your Eminence, you are embarrassing me. Your Eminence is a well-known scholar, a Prince of the Church, a Master of Eloquence — a personal friend of the Pope and of the Emperor. I am only an artist who has learned his trade from better masters. I know about the technique of fresco and painting on panels. I can draw up the plans of an average church and, with help, build it. But I can also paint a good chest to hold the belongings of whoever can pay for it. My father was an artist and I hope that my son will also be one, like the Bel-

lini family of Venice. I have earned the respect of many and the admiration of some because of my art, not my person. I hope I will also gain your respect, Eminence.'

'Excellent, Master Massolino. Now you are beginning to talk as you really are and not as you were seeming to be. If you didn't already command my respect I wouldn't have called you. I know very well whose son you are. I met your father, who

bore the same name as you, many years ago in Florence. At the time he was painting some frescoes in the Brancacci Chapel of the Carmine Church. I think it was round about 1435. I well remember he had painted his *Herod's Banquet*. No, wait; that Banquet was painted in the Baptistry in Castiglione, not in Florence. It was a miracle of resurrection that he was painting in the Brancacci Chapel. I especially liked the fresco of Original Sin in the same

The fact that artistic work was so closely related to craftsmanship led to the existence of whole families dedicated to one particular art form. These had their own workshops and studios. The Bellinis of Venice were one such family. Above, Holy Allegory *by Bellini, in the Uffizi Gallery, Florence.*

church. I remember it in detail because I particularly noticed the head of the Serpent. It was a small woman's head, and to me it looked very similar to the head

of Eve, who was a very beautiful nude indeed.'

'Your Eminence, if you will allow me to say so you have a prodigious memory and a sharpness of observation which would do credit to an artist — not to mention Your Eminence's exquisite taste which is known and praised throughout the whole of Italy,' replied Massolino, delighted by the praise which the Cardinal had heaped on his father and really amazed that he remembered so many details of a fresco which was not very well-known.

'Recognized and praised throughout the whole of Europe, I hope, Master Massolino. And if there was an element of humour in in your allusion to my good taste and to my reaction to the Eve your father painted, I have already told you that I wasn't born a cleric. I was a student here

The cultural training of the artists and the influence of Humanism supplied art with an endless source of themes from Classical mythology. Religious content was thus complemented by other cultural sources. Above, a detail from The Birth of Venus; *right,* Primavera, *both by Botticelli.*

in Siena almost thirty-five years ago. I studied Latin and Rhetoric in Florence with Master Filelfo, secretary of Cardinal Capranica in Basle, and of the Emperor's Chancellery. I've travelled all over Europe from Scotland to Switzerland, and from Austria to Bohemia. During all that time I was no more of a cleric than you are yourself. So you see, there's nothing unusual in my being able to appreciate beauty wherever it is to be found and I hope that among love-poets I have not been one of the worst.'

'I beg your pardon, Eminence, that was not what I meant and I would never have dared …'

'Yes, you would have dared because you have wit. Without that an artist is nothing. But, don't worry, I admire wit as much as I admire beauty and you have given signs of it from the outset. As regards the second matter, beauty, I hope that you can create with your hands as well as or better than your father.' The Cardinal seemed amused and delighted by the conversation. He spoke rapidly and fluently, without raising his voice.

'Your Eminence not only has wit but also wisdom.'

'I'm not so sure about that, Master Massolino, but I do have experience; I've done some useful reading and I've got eyes in my head. God put them there to be used and I don't believe he intended us to close them, not even if we are ecclesiastics. Remember what old Plato told us: that beauty is good and the greatest beauty is the highest good — that is to say, God. Now, if you like, Master Massolino we'll go down to the garden and I'll show you a Roman statue that Cardinal Capranica gave me as gift.'

They went down to the garden where the light was clear just as painters like it and the air was as pure as the famous Venetian glass. When they saw them, some priests, secretaries of the Cardinal, who were debating in the rose-garden, got respectfully to their feet and lowered their voices.

'They're honest and studious but I don't think they would appreciate your father's Eve,' laughed the Cardinal as he motioned them away towards the trees.

The life of Piero della Francesca was an excellent example of that of the 15th-century artist. He began his career in Florence and later worked in Arezzo, Rimini, Ferrara, Rome and Urbino. His work displays a capacity for combining the most spontaneous intuition with the very deepest of theoretical achievement.

'The eyes take a long time to learn, Eminence, but the intelligence which hasn't been trained takes even longer. And if I may say so, with Your Eminence's kind permission, ecclesiastical heads have their own particular difficulties because of the way they are trained.'

'In truth, Master Massolino, you put that most tactfully and elegantly,' replied Cardinal Enea Silvio, smiling. 'But not all consecrated heads are asses' heads. Some of them were intelligent enough to commission the frescoes of Saint Francis in Arezzo from your master Piero della Francesca. Others who were really exceptional were able to reach the pinnacle of your art, for I hope you haven't forgotten Brother Giovanni da Fiesole, whom they now call Fra Angelico. I'm saying that because I've been told that you worked with Brother Giovanni in Saint Mark's Convent, in your city of Florence.'

'That's quite true, Eminence, and a monk like that won't be easily forgotten. He died in Rome just over a year ago. He was working on the Nicolina Chapel and from what I've heard the frescoes of San Silvestre are really excellent. I haven't seen them myself but they would have to be truly outstanding to surpass those of the Transfiguration, Crucifixion and Annunciation of Saint Mark's Convent. If you will allow me to say so, I believe these three are among the best frescoes painted in Italy in the past twenty years. I ought to know because I worked on them and on others too, although all the credit is due to Fra Angelico and none to me.'

'You don't need my permission to hold an opinion on your own subject, Master Massolino, only your own knowledge. First and foremost Art should be made with skill and with one's whole heart. The rest is pure divine beauty which moves us and why that happens is a mystery. When a river rises it is a thread of water no greater than a curl on one of Brother Giovanni's angels. The most excellent art to begin with is no more than the exercising of a trade, but when it grows it is no less than a miracle.'

'Your Eminence talks like my Master Ghiberti and my Master Piero della Francesca. With respect to Fra Angelico's angels, I can only say to Your Eminence that if those in Paradise resemble them then I truly believe Heaven must be a good place for painters.'

'I hope it will be a good place for poets and Cardinals, too, Master Massolino.'

'Amen, Eminence, although I must admit that I can't imagine what Heaven must be like for the intelligence.'

'Don't worry about that, Master Massolino, mine will be amply rewarded by a conversation between Virgil, Dante and Petrarch. I have to admit, however, that the prize would be even sweeter if we were surrounded by Fra Giovanni da Fiesole's archangels.' The Cardinal kept his eyes fixed on a point beyond the willows round the pond and now his voice sounded sad and melancholy. 'Although for my sins I'm pretty sure that I don't deserve such a prize, I hope that in his compassion Our Lord will at least allow me some angels like Master della Robbia's.'

'I hope and firmly believe that your Eminence will have some of each and even more, like those of Ambrogio Lorenzetti and those of Simone Martini, which I would add, with Your Eminence's permission.'

'I give you that permission gladly, Master Massolino, but it is to our Lord that we both have to direct our requests.'

The Cardinal and the Artist had both fallen silent, perhaps so that they could listen to the passing of the rainbow flights of angels both were dreaming of.

Giovanni da Fiesole, known as Fra Angelico (1400-1455), was a Florentine Dominican friar and represents the "celestial" view of 15th century religious art. He painted frescoes in his own monastery (the San Marcos) and in Rome. He has always been considered a mystic.

The young man who had earlier announced Massolino's arrival in the room appeared silently and with one knee on the ground respectfully informed the Cardinal, 'Monsignor, a courier has arrived from the King of Bohemia and Hungary, and Messire Antonino, the Secretary, wants to know what he should do.'

'Let him rest and look after him. I'll talk to him tomorrow. Ask Messire Antonino to collect the letters,' answered His Eminence who seemed annoyed at the interruption. Noticing the strange expression on the Florentine's face as he watched the page withdrawing, the Cardinal explained, 'He always calls me Monsignor. I've been Cardinal for such a short time that he hasn't got used to the change of title. Anyway a Cardinal continues to be a Bishop, so calling him Monsignor is not so serious. And the King of Bohemia, he's the nephew of Emperor Friedrich. Do you know, Master Massolino, in a way I feel I was the best man at the Emperor's wedding — I headed the embassy which received the bride, Leonor of Portugal and led her to the altar in Rome. Wedding and coronation, both at the same time. And it was only five years ago — but that isn't what I wanted to talk to you about, Master Massolino; I want you to do a job for me.'

'I am at Your Eminence's service and I shall try to ensure that my ability measures up to your ideas.'

'I hope, rather, that it measures up to the wall twenty yards long and four yards high on which you are to paint a fresco. It'll be in the library of my family house at Corsignano in the mountains. It's a long job, I suppose, but it isn't your ability that worries me ... perhaps I don't have much time left, although that is in Our Lord's hands. The wall, however, will be in yours, Master Massolino.'

Master Massolino stood silent thinking of measurements and the difficulties involved. Then he spoke proudly and with assurance. 'Master Piero della Francesca is

Italian mural painting reached its greatest heights between 1450 and 1470. With its difficult technique and large dimensions, this type of painting was particularly suitable for establishing the fame of both painter and patron. Painting many square yards of space gave the artist an opportunity to develop complex themes, arranging them as a narrative and thus painting a story rather than writing it. All of which enabled the artist to demonstrate his own knowledge and affirm his social level above that of the old painter-craftsman. Right, a scene from the life of Pius II in which he is making a speech before James I of Scotland.

still at work in Arezzo on the two frescoes of Saint Francis. He's been working for five years. Between them the two, which tell the *History of the True Cross* cover more than twenty yards of wall, five yards high. Master Andrea del Castagno took five years to paint his fresco of the Last Supper and it must be at least twelve or fifteen yards long and six yards high. I've worked with them both so I know what I'm

saying. I was with Master Andrea three years ago when he was painting *The Crucifixion* in Santa Apolonia. It's a fresco more than five yards long and almost four yards high. It took us little more than a year. If I can bring four experienced assistants I shall do your fresco in three years, Eminence, and I shall put my name to that in the contract.'

Cardinal and painter went on talking enthusiastically about the project. They reviewed a complete list of the Italian frescoes of the past one hundred years, with their dimensions, subjects, painters and the number of years each had taken to complete.

The Florentine had lost all his shyness. The Cardinal seemed to know all the churches of Italy better than his palace in Siena. He was a passionate admirer of the art

Bernardino Betti, known as il pinturicchio, became famous for his elegant frivolity —even in religious themes. He adorned Siena cathedral with large frescoes depicting the life of Pius II. Above, Pius II reaching San Giovanni after his coronation.

of Taddeo Gadi, in the Santa Croce in Florence, and also of Maso di Banco and his *Miracle of the Dragon*. But most of all he delighted in Giotto.

'You are right as always, Eminence, but forgive me if I prefer the richer, more modern style of Master Antonio Pisanello in the Church of Santa Anastasia in Verona, although he has been painting for twenty years now. And when it comes to painting on panels, I've studied *The Adoration of the Three Kings* a hundred times, the one painted by Master Gentile da Fabriano thirty-five years ago. It's over five

yards long and what with the size and the placing of the figures it's almost a fresco.'

'While we're on the subject of the Three Kings, Master Massolino, if I could I'd buy the Polyptic of Pisa, by your fellow-disciple Masaccio. Your father must have taught him a lot and taught him well if he could sign that picture at the age of twenty-five.

'To these two I'd add a third Adoration of the Magi, that of the monk Lorenzo Moncaco, one of the Lorenzos which Your Eminence considers *mine*.'

'Go ahead and add it, Master Massolino, and Benozzo Gozzoli, who is working right now for Cosimo Medici on another fresco based on the Three Kings' journey.'

'Your Eminence would do me great honour by letting me deal with the same theme and so compete with such excellent masters.'

'No, Master Massolino, you are not going to paint the Three Wise Men. My fresco won't be so delicate, though it will lack netiher horses nor kings. However they won't be Wise Men or saints. I want you to paint the triumph of the Church of Rome over the Turks. It's four years now since Mahomet II conquered Constantinople. You will have only three years to paint his defeat. You will have a completely free hand in how you plan the painting and as regards perspective. I'll note down some of the ancient myths which might be useful for you and also a few pointers on theology which you will perhaps need. I have just one special request. I want both our portraits, yours and mine, to appear in this fresco.'

If the Florentine felt any curiosity about the reason behind His Eminence's whim, he showed nothing. Instead he replied,

Pope Pius II (Enea Silvio de Piccolomini), in whose honour Bernardino Betti (il pinturicchio) painted frescoes in Siena, was the almost perfect prototype of the

Renaissance Pope — educated man, writer, patron of the arts, bibliophile and collector. Above, a fresco in the Siena Cathedral Library.

smiling, 'Don't worry about that, Eminence. For myself, I'll look for a place next to a horse, dressed as a soldier which I've never been. As for you, Your Eminence, if you like I'll find a way of placing you among some Fathers of the Church. There will undoubtedly be some of them in the picture and I'll put you there with the figure of Doctor Thomas Aquinas himself.'

'That won't be necessary, Master Massolino,' replied the Cardinal laughing, 'oh no, that won't be necessary. I want you to put me next to the Emperor Constantine Palaeologus who died defending his city. Put me in as his secretary. If I have been secretary to the Emperor of the West in real life, in art I would like to be secretary to the Emperor of the East. It will be an excellent enigma for those looking at the painting. A beautiful secret which you, Master Massolino, are offering them in your painting for them to unravel. To solve the puzzle they'll have to use their ingenuity and intelligence at its sharpest. I also suggest you paint the comet which appeared in our skies last year, 1456, and which Master Toscanelli whom they call Paolo the Physician observed and drew. That way you will have something of the Three Wise Men in your picture — the star. It will also serve to remind people of that phenomenon.'

Two clerics now approached hurriedly from the bottom of the garden and knelt to kiss the enormous emerald on Cardinal Enea Silvio's episcopal ring.

'Eminence, couriers have arrived from Rome from Pope Calixtus, and it seems that the news about his health isn't good.'

'I must leave you now, Master Massolino, since serious matters must still give way to others even more serious. Go and visit Master Giovanni di Palo here in the city on my behalf. You will find him working in the Guelfi Family Chapel. Greet him in my name and tell him that I hope the Retablo which he is painting will be worthy of the Guelfis, of Siena, and of this prelate. Then go to the house of Master Vecchietta whom I revere as the best painter in Siena. He will give you my instructions and the money you need. Go in peace, Master Massolino, and work hard on those drawings. Remember you only have three years to defeat the Turks.'

The Cardinal blessed the kneeling artist and withdrew with the clerics. The garden basked in the warmth and peace of midday. On the ground some numbers which Massolino had drawn in the sand could still be seen intact. From the Palace came a murmur of voices — from time to time a single word could be distinguished: 'Eminence! Eminence!'

CONTENTS

HUMANISTS AND PRINTERS   8

    Venice, 1495   8

NAVIGATORS AND ASTRONOMERS   22

    Palos, 1492   22

SOLDIERS OF FORTUNE AND PEASANTS   38

    Treviso, 1476   38

MERCHANTS AND MONKS   54

    Nuremberg, 1463   54

PATRONS AND ARTISTS   74

    Siena, 1457   74